MW00619239

# Concert for Leah

**National prize to best novel (2010) - PEN Club of Puerto Rico**
**Fifth place, Premio Planeta (2009), Barcelona, Spain**

# CONCERT FOR *Leah*

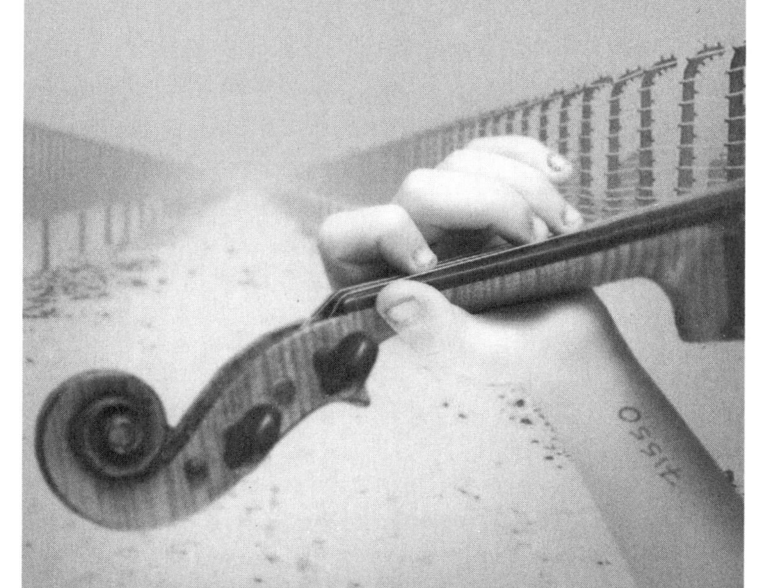


National prize to best novel (2010) - PEN Club of Puerto Rico
Fifth place, Premio Planeta (2009), Barcelona, Spain

*Concert for Leah*
ISBN 978-1-64131-159-5
© Maira Landa 2018
First English Edition and Translation: October 2018.
Printed in Bibliográficas-Biblio Services, Inc., Puerto Rico
Second Edition: March 2019
Printed in Editorial Nomos S.A., Colombia

maira.landa@gmail.com
www.mairalanda.com

País Invisible Editors/Publishers
Editor: Dr. *Emilio del Carril* (emiliodelcarril@gmail.com)
Proofreaders: *Maira Landa* and *José Cáceres Danielsen*
Artistic Concept: Dr. *Emilio del Carril*
Author's photo: *Eduardo Pérez*
Music Consultant: *José Cáceres Danielsen*
English Translation: *José Cáceres Danielsen* (caceres@josecaceres.com)
Page Design and Layout: *Eric Simó* (ericji28@yahoo.com)
Cover photo: © Zuzana Oros / DREAMSTIME, © Tamara Kulikova / DREAMSTIME
Book printing: *Bibliograficas-Biblio Services, Inc.* (info@bibliograficas.com)

Author's Literary Agent and Representative:
*Antonia Kerrigan*
Travesera de Gracia 22 1º 2ª
08021 Barcelona, Spain
Tel. (34) 932093820
www.antoniakerrigan.com

---

All Rights Reserved. No part of this publication may be reproduced, stored in a retrieval system, or transmitted in any form or by any means, electronic, mechanical, photocopying, recording, or otherwise, without the prior permission of the publisher and the author.

*To Dr. Ada Iglesias*

*Thank you for showing us the pathway to music.*
*How much you would have enjoyed this novel!*

The author
and
José Cáceres Danielsen, pianist and translator

INDEX

## First Movement – *Allegro ma non troppo*

That afternoon father arrived with the news. All four of us embraced, without uttering a word. He came with the tickets to leave in the *Saint Louis* three days later, bound for Cuba. We would have to hurry to prepare for the trip which, like an unspeakable secret, we suspected would only be one-way. The madness which had shattered our lives would be left behind.

Father felt like going for a stroll in the *Marktplatz*, the Bremen Square. We needed to get some air and behold for the very last time the surroundings of what had been our home up to then. My sister and I accompanied him, but mother decided to stay home.

We passed before the town hall, the splendid Gothic building, and reached the end of the street. There we went around the *Wesser*, which flowed serene and emitted a deep musical sound, monotonous, which reminded me of the descant in Gregorian chant. Next to the Church of San Martin there was a small lovely garden, where we would often visit. We settled ourselves beneath some immense oak trees and there, very serious, as in a thought, father said: "These trees are symbols of Germany, strong like the constancy and the immortality of our fatherland." We were surrounded by a mantle of flowers, a multicolored landscape that remained vivid in our minds.

Almost in a monologue, he spoke to us in the most measured tone that he could, so as not to alarm us too much, but with the necessary urgency and frightening graveness in his countenance:



"I beg you not to tell your friends or our neighbors about our trip. Anyone could commit an indiscretion and denounce us. We must go, before it's too late."

When we passed in front of father's medical practice, recently shut down, we made no comment. The façade was painted with black signs that read: "Death to the Jews." "We don't want Jewish doctors." His name on the bronze plaque outside was smeared with ink and could not be read. Father picked up the pace and tried hiding his face but was unable to conceal from us the tears that rolled down his cheeks.

Everything was crumbling around us. I am sure that through father's mind flashed his years of medical practice, his relationship with Oliver Lafer, the Austrian doctor who was the partner in his practice for several years, as well as the friendship and respect they felt for each other. When Oliver retired and father became the only medical practitioner, both families celebrated the day in which the bronze plaque was hung to the side of the door. How proud I felt that day! That same day, as a gift, Oliver gave us an old metronome that had belonged to his mother. It was immediately placed on top of the piano upon our return home.

We came back by the Schlachte, the medieval embankment, and took the Schnoor, the district of narrow and winding streets, which we had so often frequented, and which mother liked so much because of its shops, outdoor artists and the small cafés that set it apart. Families would stroll in that area on Sundays, for there was always music and merriment. However, on that occasion, we only encountered silence. We knew that, with all probability, it would be the last time we would walk around there.



In all the years we lived in Bremen, we had never felt rejection, but for some time an inexplicable mad-hate environment had been unleashed against us. Our lifelong neighbors, who would greet us with affection before, now shunned us. Father's patients, with whom he had been kind and charitable in many occasions, turned their backs on him. We didn't understand why.

With the proclamation of Hitler as *Führer* and Chancellor of the Reich in 1934, Nazi power was consolidated. His main objective seemed to be the elimination of Jewish presence in public life, as if were some sort of social scum. With the "law for the protection of German Blood and German Honor," we were stripped of our civil rights and classified as an "inferior race." We too were Germans!

Each person in the population was subjected to a thorough examination called *sippenbuch*, an analysis of maternal and paternal ancestors. It was enough to have a Jewish father or grandfather to be considered "impure." Thus, even those who did not consider themselves as Jews were catalogued and sanctioned. Immediately, work camps and ghettos were established to concentrate us. We understood hard times were fast approaching because, when Austria's annexation took place in 1938, thousands of lifelong Polish Jews residing in Germany were expelled. They were living in precarious conditions in-between the frontier of both countries until Poland decided to admit them.

When the Kristallnacht occurred, the "Night of Broken Glass," we were completely sure of the gravity of our situation. Throughout Germany and Austria, a fury against the Jews was unleashed. Hordes driven by hate looted and destroyed everything that represented our presence: businesses, cemeteries, synagogues. Thousands were detained, beaten, humiliated, and many murdered.

In Bremen, which was a small and peaceful city, violence raged out of control. From the window of our house we saw how some soldiers forced a group of Jews to kneel and wash the street with brushes, all while screaming and pointing their weapons at them.

One of our schoolmates, son of the town's pharmacist, was forced to paint a sing in black that read JUDE on the door of his father's pharmacy, while this one looked on. The kid cried inconsolably. When he was done, he was beaten and left unconscious on the street and the father taken into custody.

That was the day in which father declared: "We must leave, before it's too late," and our arrangements to leave Germany began.

The omnipresent Schutzstaffel or SS, Nazism's elite guard, patrolled the streets at all hours and, furthermore, was in charge of organizing the Einsatzgruppen, shock troops, composed of units of the SS and the regular police who beat and murdered Jews systematically. The Nazis were determined to create a *judenrein* Europe, cleansed of Jews, even if that meant killing us all.

Almost all houses displayed signs that read: "We don't buy from Jewish establishments." Beatings, abuses, and looting of Jewish businesses were frequent, and the arrests unjustified. Terror and suspicion were generalized.

Anti-Semitic laws were enforced one after the other. Jewish professionals could no longer practice; children and young Jews were no longer allowed to attend school. The last carriage of the tramways, which was never cleaned, was assigned to us. The rest displayed signs of "Jews not allowed."



We were forced, under penalty of arrest, to wear a yellow Star of David sewn to our clothes with a "J" in the middle. An eight PM curfew was imposed on us and we could no longer show up at theaters or restaurants. In any event, venturing out onto the street had become a very dangerous affair for us at any hour.

Many of our friends and neighbors disappeared. Many had abandoned their homes with everything in them, as we would do shortly. Of others nothing was known. It was said that they had been detained and sent to labor camps. There was talk of torture and killings, which we had difficulty believing. It was not logical for the innocent to be punished.

Father told us several ships had already left Hamburg headed for different countries on the American continent. We would go to Cuba, an island on the Caribbean, according to what he told us. For father, the trip implied numerous steps and a large part of his savings: 3.000 *reichsmarks* for the entry permits, 3.200 for the tickets and an additional 1.000 to take his surgical instruments with him. We had little money left, but it was better than staying in Germany.

We reached home in complete silence. We found mother seated at the edge of the bed, very pale and with bloodshot eyes. "Two suitcases per person," she warned us. "Only take what is absolutely necessary. We don't know how long we'll be away."



How to pack all our belongings there? How could we leave behind our little treasures, our experiences? How to determine what each one would take proved a mystery. Not knowing where to start, I looked at my mother. "To her, more than to us, it must be harder," I thought. When she finished packing, I noticed that the pictures and family mementos almost filled one of her suitcases.

My sister sat at the piano, I presume to calm down, and played one of her favorite pieces, Liszt's *Liebestraum No. 3*. Mother stood next to her and placed a hand on her left shoulder. Father, captivated by the music, came into the drawing room, ready to listen to her. I sat on the armchair's rest and leaned my head on his shoulder. The house was filled with melodies.

Music had always been an important element in our family. Mother taught piano to some of the kids in the neighborhood. It was with her that we took our first steps with musical notes, almost as soon as we came into the world. Rachel liked the piano and played it well, but I was more attracted to the violin, until it became my real passion. Father did not play any instrument, but was most knowledgeable and very discerning.

My teacher was Madame Suzette Lamar, a retired French violinist, strict and demanding, with whom I had a very close relationship. A year ago, she told my parents she was convinced

I would become a soloist —as I had set out to become— that my talent had impressed her and that she had never had a student so devoted to music.

She suggested that they buy me a better instrument as soon as possible and volunteered to prepare me for the entrance examination to the Berlin Music Conservatory, where she believed the teachers that I would require in my next stage were to be found. Mother talked to a great friend of hers who lived in that city, and they agreed that I would stay with her while my studies lasted. I was ecstatic with happiness. I would become a soloist!



Madame Lamar took it upon herself to find an adequate violin for me, until a French luthier friend of hers told her that he had just received a Guarneri belonging to a woman from the Russian royalty, fallen on hard times due to the Bolshevik Revolution, and urgently in need of money. The luthier knew the instrument very well because he had restored it a couple of years ago. The price was very attractive, so father and I went to Paris to try and buy it.

When I first held it in my hands, I could not believe it was two hundred years old. The violin was beautiful, with its box of a glossy russet varnish. I checked the tuning, placed it in position, rested my cheek on its noble wood and readied myself to play it. When I plucked its strings, and began to rub them with the bow, a current ran through my senses. It was the most wonderful sound, vigorous and harmonious, that I had ever heard. The melody occurred almost spontaneously, my fingers slid effortlessly. "Now I understand why the Guarneri was Paganini's favorite instrument, why he loved his Cannone so much," I thought. Father was moved and smiled.

We looked at each other and we both knew then that we had finally found it. That would be "my" violin.

"Did you notice its sound? Its tone is unmistakable, more powerful and more metallic than the Stradivarius. Guarneri used a special kind of wood and treated it with layers of varnish, a secret technique that has not been surpassed by later violin makers. I prefer a Guarneri to any other. This is a great instrument," the luthier told me with pride.

He showed us, in the inside of the resonance box, the unmistakable seal of its creator: "*Giuseppe Guarnerius fecit Cremonae anno 1737 IHS.*" He explained to us that what remained of his original production did not exceed two hundred and fifty violins in the entire world. I listened to him spellbound.

"What do the initials at the end mean?" I asked him.

"Guarnerius was a very religious man and was known as 'di Gesu,' which in Italian means 'of Jesus.' IHS means Jesus in Greek, but abbreviated. It was his way of venerating the Holy Spirit. In other words, could it not be an instrument for a Jewish violinist, don't you think? I trust that's not important for you, as it hasn't been for the great Jewish violinists," he told me, with a smile.

Father laughed at the luthier's clever remark, also a Jew.

Once the transaction was concluded, he handed it over to me in a lovely glossy blue leather case, on which interior cover I proudly wrote right there and then: "This violin belongs to Leah."

We returned to our home in Bremen, beaming with happiness. During the entire journey I clasped my new instrument in my arms, with a perennial smile on my face, in disbelief that it was mine. I remember father's satisfaction on seeing me in such ecstasy. I can't recall how many times I hugged him and thanked him for buying it for me. All he answered was: "I believed in you, my child. Now prove to me that you really deserve it. When I see you debuting on stage and proudly applaud you, I will know that this enormous effort was worthwhile."



My Guarneri became the meaning of my life. It was always by my side, practicing without rest. Becoming a soloist had turned into an obsession, my *leitmotiv.* Madame Lamar taught me to understand my instrument and declared: "This violin is marvelous; it deserves a special performer, like you."

We worked very hard that entire year. I was almost ready to present myself at the Conservatory, with the application for admission, when the situation in Germany became intolerable for the Jews and father arrived with the trip's news. We had to go. Now, my plans and those of my family would have to wait for better times. In spite of it all, I felt much better knowing that I could take my violin with me, but felt sorry for Rachel. The piano would stay behind, along with all the furniture and the rest of our belongings, like custodians of our memories. Mother cheered us promising that, once settled in Cuba, we would buy a piano and that I would also be able to continue with my plans till I reached my goal. "It's only a delay, but you will see that everything will turn out okay. Besides, perhaps we can return to Bremen, to our house," she told us.

Thousands of notes hovered in my mind, which at that time arranged in a spontaneous and unexpected manner. They would transmute into a recondite sonority, always different, that would take shape according to my feelings. Sometimes, two or three shy *neumes* of a simple melody would insinuate themselves in a tune that delighted me. At others, they would amalgamate in a complex pentagram, becoming a torment. The worst part was that no one seemed to hear my internal music. When I finally dared tell my sister, much more practical than myself, she looked at me mockingly and said that I was crazy beyond repair. Those terrible times turned out to be very musical for me.



During the three following days we moved about the house in slow motion, hardly speaking to one another, with a serious countenance and crestfallen, as if everyone was meditating the move we were about to make. The sleepless nights seemed endless. The melodies that hovered about me would manifest themselves at their own *tempo*.

The afternoon before our departure, I spent several hours in the living room of our house, where every Sunday we welcomed guests and, prior to serving dinner, we enjoyed musical soirées. The room's focus was the Steinway grand piano that father gave mother as a wedding present. Next to it was the music stand where I would place my scores. Hung in the walls were pictures of our grandparents, of our parents' wedding, and of the two of us during different moments of our childhood. In the corner, the pedestal radio in-between mother and father's armchairs, sunken by the memories of the innumerable nights of happy family life. The wide windows invited the images and aromas of our garden to enter our home.

In the kitchen, the short white curtains with green stripes on the window, the white crockery carefully arranged on the shelf, the shiny copper pots and the coffee grinder, from which its emanation awoke us each morning. I longed for that room to jealously guard in its nooks and corners, those delicious smells that belonged to us, because they were only ours, in the event we might return someday. I evoked the aromas of the honey pies that mother always prepared for Rosh Hashanah and the tasty *cholent* for the *Shabbath*. How mother insisted that we eat, especially me who was of a poor appetite, because there were so many hungry children in the world! How I would recall her words later throughout my entire life! In that beloved house, our home, our laughs and the dreams of our family would remain immured; soon to only become an echo of the past.

Dawn caught me standing before the window of my room, clutching my violin. Motionless there practically till the hour of our departure, I tried to engrave in my retinas the silhouette of the immense tree, of a wide trunk and plentiful branches that proudly presided over our garden sheltering me beneath its shadow. Surely, on many occasions it had regaled in the melodies bestowed upon it with my music. I was going to miss it so much!

I wished to impregnate my pores with the perfume of that garden, witness to my hours of bliss. Deep down within me burst a polyphony and a tessitura of great density that came from afar in surges, progressively more defined. A sad *lied*, infinitely sad.

“Joseph, girls, we’ve got to go,” mother urged us.

We brought the suitcases out and father hastily closed the door behind him, without turning back. Hans —the priest of the Christian Church in our neighborhood and a friend and patient of father′s— had offered to take us in his car, an old dark green Opel. He said that if soldiers saw a family with a priest, dressed in his cassock, they wouldn't suspect that we were Jewish and wouldn't stop us.

Both became friends after Hans started going to father's practice to get treated for stomach issues. Their friendship grew throughout the years, even though they professed different religions. Our priest friend expressed that we all believed in the same God, only viewed from a different perspective. A regular visitor in our house as well as an assiduous audience in our Sunday soirées, both he and father played chess for hours and talked a lot. We noticed that recently he didn't wear his cassock during the visits to our house. Perhaps he did this to not compromise himself.



As night faded, on the 12th of May 1939, we left our house in Bremen and began the two-hour drive towards the port of Hamburg, in the middle of a dense fog and a persistent drizzle. Nobody spoke during the entire ride; each absorbed in their own thoughts.

Father was seated next to Hans. Mother, Rachel and I sat in the back seat where we barely could accommodate ourselves. I glanced at father, tall, slender, so distinguished looking, and suddenly realized that his hair had turned grey. He was a good man, devoted to his patients and to his family. He looked tired.

Mother had her eyes closed, as if she didn't want to see what we were leaving behind. Her blue eyes contrasted with her auburn hair. When she laughed two dimples would form on her cheeks. I was amazed at her equanimity and wisdom, for she seemed to know what needed to be done always. She dropped everything to marry father: country, religion, family, and even an incipient career as a pianist.

My sister and I were opposite poles. Rachel was fifteen years old, always happy and very pretty, like a replica of mother, but of a weak character. Father would comment that I had a languid stare and that my sister possessed a serene semblance, like the two sisters in the Bible, the daughters of Lavan. Being two years older and inheriting father's pronounced Jewish traits brought me great problems at the time. Perhaps being the eldest made me more mature than my sister, and very stubborn. My parents claimed that I would lock myself up in my own world. Jealous of Rachel at the time —for she was the center of attention— the boys hardly looked at me because I was not as attractive as her.

The unmistakable smell of saltpeter brought us out of our reveries and announced that we were nearing our destination.

The *Saint Louis* rose majestically on dock 76 of the port of Hamburg, deserted at that early hour, except for the SS doing their rounds. We decided to board separately, so as not to attract attention. First Rachel, and then mother.

Hans stayed with us for another half an hour, until father and I decided to board the ship. We hugged him and thanked him for his invaluable help. He responded with a half-smile and a subtle blessing gesture with his right hand. "May God be with you," he said.

I felt a horrible shiver when father took me by the hand. His was frozen and quivering. That determined man, whom we all considered so strong, was disconcerted and afraid.

We boarded the ship, trying to feign composure. Hans watched us from a distance. No one stopped us.

On the ramp, a man took pictures of the passengers while they boarded. He only seemed interested with those who were poorly dressed. Afterwards some said he was from the Gestapo and that, with all likelihood, the pictures would be published in the German newspapers to show the world how fled the subhuman scum, the *untermenschen*. That is what we were called.



The *Saint Louis* carried over nine hundred passengers, almost all German Jews, some fugitives from the Nazis, and many women alone with their children. Some had left their husbands in concentration camps and others their husbands waited for them in Cuba.

The three double chimneys, in black, red and white, erect, smoking amidst the fog, offered a gloomy aspect. Three of the five floors were below sea level. At the top of the mast an immense red flag undulated, with the dreaded black swastika in the middle. The line Hamburg-America, HAPAG, to which the *Saint Louis* belonged, was under the German government's control. Except for the Captain, the crew, composed of more than a hundred men, all wore the Nazi insignia on their uniforms. To salute, they stood to attention with an extended arm and cried out *Heil* Hitler. It was rumored that amongst them there were members of the *Abwehr*, the Nazi secret service, but we didn't know for certain whom these might be. The Captain, Gustave Schroeder, was a middle-aged German, with thin lips, crowned with a small mustache. His grey hair and tanned skin contrasted with his clear blue eyes. He walked with steady strides and seemed to be a man with a controlled, measured character.

We were assigned cabins 111 and 113, on deck B of the gunwale. They were adjoining and small, with simple but comfortable furniture. From the sheets and towels emanated a delicious lavender smell. What Rachel and I liked the most were the two skylights that allowed us to see the ocean.

At eight o'clock, on the 13th of August 1939, the ship's sirens sounded several times, in its imminent departure from port. The city of Hamburg was in a festive mood, all lit up for its 750th anniversary. The *Saint Louis* began its slow and inexorable march towards the open sea, while the city lights became smaller by degrees and disappeared in the distance.

We passengers were on deck. Rachel and I, in our parents' arms, cried in silence. Suspended in time, with our eyes fixed on the land that moved away, we tried to capture forever our country's silhouette, framed by a lovely starry night and interrupted by the ominous red flag with the swastika that floated free and flapped at the top of the mast.

And, once again, music surfaced as a bad omen. All night long the intense *vibrato* of a dry recitative did not abandon me, with its hammering of tones and semitones which only I heard, repeatedly.

The loudspeakers interrupted the scenery. The Captain summoned us all to the Tanzplatz, the activities salon on deck B, for a welcome reception. We were petrified when we stumbled upon Hitler's picture and an immense swastika in a preferential place of the salon. Besides, several crew members sang *Horst-Wessel* out loud, a very popular Nazi song. The Captain hurriedly came up to them, closed the piano, and ordered them to withdraw. The men left the salon at the cry of *Heil* Hitler, while casting looks of hate all around them.

We tried on our behalf to not applaud the Captain, who was incensed.

Next to me was a middle-aged Russian man whose face was crimson from rage. Staggering, he walked to one of the salon's corners and dropped into an armchair. He gasped, was short of air and seemed to be on the verge of collapse. Father approached him to ask him what was wrong and if he needed any help. I remained near father. Something about that man woke up the compassion in me.



Father suggested that we go on deck to get some fresh air and, especially, to get away from some of the Nazi crew still in the Tanzplatz. We settled into the deck chairs, only us three. Almost on the verge of tears and with shaky hands he told us about his odyssey. He had just come out of a labor camp and that's why he couldn't stand the expressions of those Nazis.

His name was Ivan Skolof. Russian-born, he had lived for many years in Germany, where his wife and children were also from. The man told us he was a watchmaker by profession and that, for being Jewish, had been arrested and sent to Dachau where he suffered unimaginable atrocities. Horrifying stories of the work camps, of tortures and killings poured out of him. A friend of his, with government connections, had interceded on his behalf. The Nazis released him on the condition he leave Germany immediately and never return. Otherwise, he and his family would once again be interned, and this time death would await all of them. To pay for the fare on the *Saint Louis*, Skolof was forced to sell all his possessions, leaving his wife and two children to the care of his parents. Once established in Cuba, he would save all he could to have them join him. His sadness was overwhelming; his eyes reflected a sheer desolation which I'd never seen before. I clearly understood why that man couldn't stand the Nazis' behavior.

Father and I stayed with him for a long while until he calmed down. What he related was terrifying and worse than what we had imagined. The situation in Germany was alarming.



We immediately realized that we had made the right decision on leaving our country.

We told mother and Rachel everything Mr. Skolof had recounted. We agreed we'd keep him company and show solidarity towards him. Sometimes we invited him to join us for dinner. Other times, father would often sit by his side to chat; we would greet him and tried to cheer him up. He reciprocated gratefully. He was a noble man, humble, and very hurt.

Some of the passengers took it upon themselves to organize musical soirées in the Tanzplatz. Mother volunteered to play the piano and asked me to join her with my violin.

We created a rather disjointed group because some of the participants didn't know much music. Christened as "The Traveling Musicians," we at least entertained the rest of the passengers and had lots of fun doing it. Mark, a handsome 18-year old man who was traveling alone, carried an accordion with him. We both rehearsed some pieces. Mark wasn't too accomplished musically, but was easy to get along with. He told me that I played the violin very well and that I was beautiful. We talked about continuing our friendship when we got to Cuba. Sometimes we sat on the deck chairs to talk and, suddenly, caught mother watching us from a distance, pretending she was knitting. She realized that I really liked Mark.

Days went by in a prosaic normalcy, which increased as we neared America. We would distract ourselves at the movies, listening to music or by looking at the foamy wake the ship left in its sailing. We began to feel safe. In several days' time we'd reach our new home.



Little by little, we made friends with some of the passengers and met several of the crew who were kind to us. There were two rabbis on board: Abraham Leibovitz and Yitzhak Weitz, to whom the Captain had given permission to officiate our services. On occasions, the Tanzplatz would be turned into a synagogue for the conservative Jews, but we'd sit with our backs to Hitler's photo, so as not to see him. The poor rabbi had him right in front. The orthodox would gather in the first-class dance hall or in the gymnasium. There they didn't have the portrait problem.

We were struck by two girls who traveled alone: Renata, age seven, and Evelyn, age five. Their father, a famous German doctor, was waiting for them in Cuba while the mother had stayed behind in Germany. An elderly couple had offered to take care of them during the crossing. Mother always kept an eye on them to make sure they were well, and we would often play with them to entertain them. Many a time I wondered if they'd be frightened at night or if they missed their parents. They were very little.

Rumors spread that there were German spies among the crew. Particularly, the gossip would point to Otto Schiendick as the main one, a sinister character, of short stature, plumb and with bulging eyes, whose manners left a lot to be desired and who didn't hide his obvious dislike for the Jews.

When we sailed before the coastline of the Azores, the Captain announced through the loudspeakers that we were halfway to Cuba. The swaying of the waves was very strong and the *Saint Louis* lurched. Many had to visit the infirmary with seasickness and vomiting. Father and other passengers, also doctors, volunteered to help.



We would frequently hear comments as to what we would find in Cuba: that they wore light clothes there because it was very hot all year round, that its music was very lively, that the food was different from our own and that there were lots of sweet fruit, unknown in Europe. Everyone speculated as to how that place might be that seemed so exotic, unable to imagine it. We were anxious to get there.

"Father, father, open!" we knocked repeatedly at the cabin door.

"What's the matter?"

"A man fainted. Please, come quickly to the Tanzplatz."

Father came immediately. The ship's doctor was already there, but there was nothing further to be done. Mr. Weiss, who traveled with his wife, died of a heart attack. As is mandatory in the Torah, the body could not be touched for the first eight minutes after death occurred. Afterwards, the body was placed on the floor with its feet facing the door. The widow lit several candles, covered the skylights with some cloths and recited the corresponding prayers. The scene was moving and at the same time incongruous: a Jewish funeral, with Hitler's portrait as witness. Rachel and I were impressed. It was our first encounter with death; so unexpected, so close.

Hours later, the *Saint Louis* stopped in the middle of the ocean, while the Captain and his first officer paid their respects to the widow, standing in alert, their caps in hand. They handed her a map indicating the place where we presently were. Since there was nowhere to preserve the body, it had to be cast into the sea, wrapped in a well sewn sac.



Rabbi Leibovitz conducted a simple ritual in Hebrew, while Mrs. Weiss wept in silence and the rest of us stood brokenhearted. Sadness floated in the air, but we noticed with annoyance that some members of the crew observed from afar with an irreverent and mocking smile.

The wind whipped with force and the sky turned to an intense red, as if a storm approached. Stars were absent from the night. Figurations of notes, intervals, flats and sharps crowded haphazardly in my head, like a *mezza voce*, until acquiring a compact tone. My fibers vibrated out of control to the disquieting rhythm of a requiem.

It must have been a premonition, since on that dawn the first cable that would unleash the odyssey was received. The Paris newspapers informed that Cuba would not take in any more refugees and that behind the *Saint Louis,* two more ships were headed to the island: the *Orduña*, British, and the *Flandre*, of French registry.

The Captain, anticipating what could occur, hastily appointed a Passenger's Committee and chose father as its director, who was restrained, even-handed and was used to facing tense situations due to his profession. A meeting was immediately convened to maintain the passengers informed. No one had answers for the countless questions that cropped up. The agony began.

I listened to father argue with vehemence before the passengers that there was no need to worry because we all had the official entry permits for Cuba, negotiated with the OBERRAT, a very old and respected Jewish organization. Besides, the island's authorities had issued and charged for them. He said that it no doubt was some kind of misunderstanding, that everything would be cleared as soon as we reached the island. The Captain reiterated numerous times that he himself would negotiate our situation with the Cuban authorities.



Nevertheless, I knew father very well and intuited an underlying anxiety in his voice. He was not altogether convinced of what he claimed, I sensed. The Captain didn't want to worry us either. They both were in sync, in the same melodic tone, like my violin and me. Fear that we would be returned to Germany floated ominously among us.

At dawn the next day, the siren once again ululated deafening. Ivan Skolof, the Russian that we had met on the first day, had jumped overboard. In my head reverberated his stories regarding the atrocities the Nazis perpetrated against the Jews. "He couldn't bear the possibility of returning to Germany," I thought.

The Saint Louis turned on the same spot for over an hour, unsuccessfully. The Captain decided to continue on with the trip while many of us remained on the stern, in silence, with our eyes fixed on the foamy wake that the ship formed. I imagined that, like me, the others tried to understand Skolof's despair. I don't know if some succeeded or not, but I felt a great sadness for him and thought about his family. At that moment, my heartbeats composed their own syncopated music.

That afternoon the Captain asked father, as representative of the Passengers' Committee, to accompany him to Mr. Skolof's cabin to pick up his belongings and to later send them on to his family. There were very few clothes in his suitcase, some pictures of his wife and children and several letters addressed to them. The last one was dated that same day, inside an open envelope with the name and address of his wife in Germany. In the letter, Skolof told her about his agony in the Dachau Camp, the terror, the tortures, and the humiliation that he had suffered. He also recounted the medical experiments they'd done on him. Preferring death to returning to that hell, Skolof signed off by saying that he loved them and asked for forgiveness.

Father returned to the cabin, destroyed. He told us what had happened and the contents of Mr. Skolof's farewell letter. I thought about the suffering that he must have gone through and the fear he must have felt. I felt a profound sadness for him.

At the end of the day, the *Saint Louis* had lost its voices. In the dining hall, full as usual, could only be heard the monotonous sound of plates, glasses and cutlery. The cinema was left deserted and there was not a soul on the Tanzplatz. We all took early refuge in our cabins, while the ship glided serene before the lighthouse of the Bahamas and came closer to our destination. The Nazi crew was making fun about us without any pretense and made a gesture with their hands around their necks as if to tell us that we were going to die.

That night my sister and I were very scared. We took shelter in our parents' cabin who were also awake. When we lived in Germany, the four of us would always come together to talk when something worried us, as well as on happy occasions. For an instant I forgot where I was but, when father tried to cheer us and to outline plans for when we reached Cuba, I heard a terrifying dissonant sound in my head, which dimmed his words and chased away my sleep.

The following day went by monotonously and full of uncertainty. The ship sailed in front of the United States' Florida coastline. From the deck, we watched the landscape and asked ourselves what would happen when we reached Cuba.



At four in the morning on the 27th of May, the siren announced our imminent entry into port. To our left, no too far off, we could see Havana, still lethargic in the darkness. Its buildings revealed a grand city. To our right, an enormous lighthouse stood out, with a rotating light that seemed to guide us from the top of a cliff, which rested defiantly on the sea. It was part of a very old and imposing edification, surrounded by stone walls, through which hundreds of menacing canons appeared. Afterwards we learnt that it was El Morro, a fortress built in the seventeenth century for the city's defense.

We witnessed a magnificent sunrise. The sky lavished us with a multicolored spectacle, with blurred clouds in the middle of an intense blue, with streaks of orange of various gradations. The coast's tropical scenery with its hues of greens and turquoise water, perhaps an illusion, made us think that nothing bad could occur to us in such a beautiful place. While we were in rapture before that paradisiacal spectacle, the ship continued its slow advance towards the port. In my interior, a playful scherzo, in an antiphonal impromptu, conjugated as *leitmotiv* with the images.

While having breakfast, we could see the city through the dining room's large window. I listened to animated conversations, in-between laughs and jocular remarks, regarding what they'd do upon landing. A young man said he was going to eat bananas until he exploded and another one was sure to fall in love with a Cuban woman, because he had been told they were very pretty. For the first time in a long time, I heard with pleasure my own laugher and noticed that the rest behaved normally. I wondered if that representation, half-way between fantasy and reality, was a spell to forget our fears.

The *Saint Louis* stopped in the middle of the bay, facing Havana. They did not allow it to dock at the harbor as was the norm. A patrol boat of the Cuban authorities approached, and several officers came on board to check everyone's documents. In spite of the Captain's protests for the delay that such complicated procedure would cause, the director of the Cuban medical team insisted on interviewing all the passengers, regardless of the time it would take, to ascertain that there were no contagious diseases. Meanwhile, they hoisted the yellow flag of quarantine.

With the intention to lift our spirits, mother addressed our group, "The Traveling Musicians," and enticed us to perform the festive German tune of "*Freut euch des Lebens,*" "Rejoice, You Are Alive." Lots of passengers gathered in the Tanzplatz and sang loudly. Doctor Glauner, one of the officers on board, escorted the Cuban officials to the dining hall, where the interviews would be conducted. There he handed them a folder, with all the required information and where it stated that everyone on board was in good physical and mental health. He also guaranteed that we would not become a social blight for the island of Cuba.

The Cubans spoke loudly, were congenial and gesticulated with vivaciousness. Although their skin was quite white, they were darker than us. Two colored men caused quite a sensation. We had never seen such dark skin, which shone beneath the sun. Their hair was kinky and strong. Since we looked at them with curiosity, they smiled back at us, showing us their immaculate white teeth.



Several patrol boats circled the Saint Louis, along with some smaller vessels carrying some of the passengers' relatives, whom they tried to greet. Through some megaphones, the Cuban police ordered them to keep at a distance.

That evening the anxiety was widespread. Dinner was served early and the two rabbis conducted a prayer service.

The Cuban medical authorities took two days to finish their inspection and it was only then that they lowered the quarantine flag. Immigration officials then came on board to check the passports, the entry permits and the landing cards. Next to the red "J," which identified us as Jews, they stamped a green "R" for refugee. Everyone was handed a card to collect their luggage on deck. Everything seemed to be in order.

A few hours later the *Orduña* arrived, a smaller ship than the *Saint Louis,* also policed by the island's patrol boats and surrounded by smaller vessels full of relatives. It waited for its turn at a certain distance from us, also at the bay's entrance. The ships sounded their respective sirens and the passengers exchanged greetings from afar.

Through the loudspeakers, Cuban immigration officers called five passengers by their names for them to abandon the *Saint Louis* and board a smaller boat that would take them to port. One of them was a very mysterious-looking lady, who moved about the ship always garbed in black, and traveled alone. The others were two couples. We all thought that would be the proper procedure to follow and that soon the rest would also be called.

In frenzied activity, we hauled our suitcases from one place to another and prepared for imminent docking. The deck chairs had been removed to facilitate the never-ending movement of people, and there was a long line of suitcases on the gangways. Around mid-morning, about fifty had concluded their paperwork and waited at the top of the ladder, ready to be carried ashore. The Cuban officials interrupted the process in an abrupt manner, ordered everyone to return to their cabins and abandoned the *Saint Louis* without any explanation.

We saw those in the *Orduña* disembark in the late hours of the afternoon, leaving the port that same night without a problem. The following day, the *Flandre* arrived, greeted us with its siren and placed itself in the same spot. Hours later, its passengers had disembarked the ship and it too sailed off the bay. Those of us on the *Saint Louis* were becoming more and more restless. We couldn't understand in what sort of complex web we had fallen into.

As time passed, the Captain convened the Passengers' Committee to an emergency meeting. For three hours they were unable to figure out what was happening, of finding a solution. Schroder tried to obtain information, but he was only fed rumors, nothing concrete. Father returned to the cabin fuming, where mother and us two waited anxiously for him. He said: "A few hours ago, the Captain received a cable from the President of Cuba, Federico Laredo Brú. He refuses to admit us because he says that the Minister of Immigration gave us our visas behind his back and stole the money. The relief organizations for refugees are in negotiations with the island's government, but suspect that what the Cubans want is more money. This is outrageous! They charged us for the visas and for entry into the country and now they trade us like cattle."



"Joseph, why did the other two ships sail off port and were able to disembark its passengers without any problems? It must have been a mistake or some mix-up with the procedures because the *Saint Louis* has almost a thousand passengers," mother said.

"No, dear, it's just that the *Orduña* is a British vessel and the *Flandre* a French one. They don't want us because we're German, because we're Jews. It's a political issue and one of discrimination. That's what's going on," father exclaimed appalled and at the same time hopelessly dropping himself into an armchair. I was very distressed on seeing him so outraged. I observed the deep bags under his bloodshot eyes.

Mother tried to say something, but was unable to do so. Rachel remarked sarcastically that, jumping overboard was not such a bad idea after all. Mother reprimanded her severely and told us:

"Never say that again. Never lose your faith, never!"

I remained silent, absorbed in my own world. My senses were inundated by a persistent *rondeau*, a French *lai*, with a melodic tempo and constant tremolo. I was assailed by sadness.

Passengers stood in line for hours to send wires to their relatives, to the organizations in charge of helping Jewish refugees and to all those who could intercede on our behalf. Father told us that dispatches had been sent to President Roosevelt, to Cardinal Spellman of New York, to Judge Pecora of the Supreme Court of the United States and, the majority, to the President of Cuba. Desperate messages of the *Saint Louis* reached the entire world.

The next day, Renata and Evelyn's father came on board, escorted by three Cuban policemen, with a written authorization from the island's Cuban authorities to take his daughters with him. When they said goodbye to us and we saw the girls so happy to be reunited with their father, we felt a great relief that those children were leaving the ship.

Four days later, the *Saint Louis* was still anchored in the middle of the Havana bay. With spirits running high, fights broke out over anything insignificant. To exacerbate the situation, the heat of over one hundred degrees —to which we were not used to— was dry and unbearable.

The Captain received several wires that informed us that massive protest marches were taking place around the world, in solidarity with us. We also learnt that reporters from the *New York Times* and other U.S. newspapers had landed in Cuba and had published articles requesting Cuba to allow us to disembark. The island's authorities remained firm in their refusal.

That very same day a cable was received that informed us that the German newspaper, *Der Stuermer,* demanded in its editorial that we immediately be returned to Germany and sent to the concentration camps. That reaffirmed what was clear to us all: no one wanted us. We became more and more frightened.

Suddenly, we had become a tourist attraction. In the midst of the din and frivolity, as if it were a fair, quay binoculars and field glasses were rented out on the Havana harbor to look at us, newspaper salesmen shouted out the latest news, and journalists were on standby day and night, in case some new development took place.



The monotony was noticeable and the heat unbearable. Passengers wandered from one place to another not knowing what to do or expect. Some remarked sarcastically that the *Saint Louis* had become a floating concentration camp.

On June 1st, an emissary from the Cuban President came on board to inform the Captain that the island's government demanded that we leave the port immediately. If we refused to leave, the Cuban Navy would use force, even if this meant taking up arms against us.

Schroeder was nervous and very worried. He got together with father privately and told him, confidentially, that he had asked the authorities for a few hours of grace in which he would try to go on land to meet with the Cuban President. Meanwhile, he had no other option than to order the engines started. He asked him to inform the Committee of what was happening and try to allay everyone's fears. Time was of the essence, now.

As soon as the noise from the motors was evident, many started to scream desperately and others tried jumping overboard. The Cuban policemen that were on board fired in the air, forcing them to move back. The situation was about to get out of hand, but the Passengers' Committee could control it with the help of the two rabbis on board. Some had to be sedated by the ship's doctors.



Meanwhile, the Captain had slipped off the ship incognito, without his uniform, and was already in Havana. There he was received by Mr. Arthur Meyer, representative of the American Joint Distribution Committee, a relief organization for refugees, who had arrived in Cuba from New York several days earlier to negotiate with the island's authorities.

First, they met with the German Consul, who refused to mediate before the Cuban government. He claimed the Jews were not welcome on the island and would not be accepted. They then tried to reach the Presidential Palace to speak with Laredo Brú, but this one refused to meet with them. Finally, they went to Fulgencio Batista's office, the Army Chief of Staff, but all they accomplished was to meet with one of his assistants, who quickly dismissed them without giving them any hope and further said not to persist, that the decision was firm and final.

Schroeder returned to the ship a couple of hours later, disheartened. With these actions he had put himself in evidence vis-a-vis the Nazis and knew what this meant for his career, his personal safety and that of his family. A cable from HAPAG awaited him, ordering him to turn the *Saint Louis* around and immediately return to Europe.

The Captain, whose knowledge of Spanish was quite good, showed father a copy of Cuba's *Diario de la Marina* that he had bought in Havana. In its full-page editorial, it was against admitting the Jews of *Saint Louis* because "almost a thousand refugees would substantially increase the already high unemployment rate we have on the island." He also had with him the newspapers *Avance* and *Alerta*. Both echoed the same sentiment, in the same tone of hate and injustice. He told father in a defeated tone: "Doctor, I'm sorry. We've lost the battle, unless a miracle happens..."



That evening, the rabbis performed the prayers. The passengers were despondent and hardly spoke. Father and mother tried to calm Rachel and me, but everything was futile. The departure from Cuba was imminent and our destiny looked more uncertain and dreary. The next day, early in the morning, two immigration officers from the island came on board and issued permits to six persons to remain in Cuba. They were immediately taken to port. We did not know why or who they were, but it was rumored that they had Cuban citizenship. Others said that their relatives had paid large amounts of money to the government. Before leaving the ship, the highest-ranking officer spoke to the Captain and father to tell them in *sotto voce* that he was sorry for what was happening; that he was only carrying out orders and that wished us good luck.

Mr. Meyer, who had accompanied the Captain in his negotiations in Havana, came onboard. He asked to the Captain permission to talk to the passengers. Deeply moved, he told us not to lose faith and that the relief organizations for refugees —with the Joint Committee at the head— were not going to allow for our return to Germany. He reiterated that the eyes of the world were upon us and that lots of people would continue to work to find a solution to our problem. "The *Saint Louis* must leave the harbor now. We have been given orders and they must be obeyed. That will give us some leeway to negotiate with Cuba or with other countries. Have faith, that God will not abandon us," he expressed deeply moved. The passengers applauded him. All of us, without exception, had tears in our eyes. His words acted like a balsam, an injection full of hope for almost a thousand human beings sunken in despair and anguish.



In an aside, he told the Captain and father that he was furious because the Joint Committee had just learnt that, eight days before the *Saint Louis* had set sail from the port of Hamburg, the Cuban President had signed a decree invalidating the visas granted to the Jewish immigrants. The HAPAG had knowledge of this, but allowed for the ship to reach the island anyway, apparently to collect the ticket money. The Captain asked father not to share that information with the rest of the passengers, so as not to further exacerbate the mood. The situation was extremely tense.

The Captain informed Mr. Mayer that he would take the *Saint Louis* to the Florida coasts, with the hope that the American authorities would take us in. If that was unsuccessful, at least some days would elapse that would let the Joint do some progress in their effort. We were ready to weigh anchor. We would have to leave Cuba and return to Germany. The Captain announced through the loudspeakers that we were headed for Florida, in one last attempt for the United States to admit us. Some of the crew members objected, but the Captain said he would assume all the responsibility for his decision.

In spite of knowing the dire economic situation the United States was in, the closure of thousands of factories and the high levels of unemployment, a tenuous hope, mixed with skepticism, reigned among us. We needed to believe that charity would prevail above the material.

We left in the late afternoon of the 2nd of June, escorted by twenty-six Cuban police boats that illuminated the *Saint Louis* with powerful searchlights and from where they aimed their weapons at us. The small vessels, full of relatives, kept at a distance without being able to come any closer, while they witnessed heartbroken how we slowly left the bay. In the distance, a crowd watched from the port. We gazed impotent at how that piece of land that till then we had thought would be our salvation moved away. We felt vulnerable, adrift.



Some of the crew members —emboldened by the news and by the Captain's decision— sang Nazi songs in the Tanzplatz. One of them read out loud a list of charges that they would level against him once they had disembarked in Germany. Another announced at the top of his voice what was coming to us Jews "so as not to forget that you are scum." We witnessed the scene outraged, but we did not dare answer back so as not to further irritate them.

In repeated occasions, Schroeder exposed himself by defending us, something inconceivable for a German of his rank. By then no one had any doubts that some of the crew members were Nazi spies, for which father feared that at any moment they would kill the Captain, himself or some passenger, and bring about a large-scale revolt. Spirits were running high in both camps. He cautioned the members of the Passengers' Committee to be on guard, alert, on the lookout as to what might occur.

On June 4th, at dawn, we arrived before the city of Miami, which could be seen without the use of binoculars. As opposed to Havana, it was not a pretty place, but rather a barren plain, with few buildings, tenuous lights and little movement. Two patrol boats of the American Coast Guard intercepted our ship and, through some megaphones, ordered us to leave the territorial waters of the United States. A couple of American airplanes flew overhead several times at a low altitude. The *Saint Louis* moved towards the open sea.



The following day a message was received from the Joint Committee informing us that the Cuban President had declared he considered the possibility of admitting the *Saint Louis* refugees, but on condition that they stay on Isle of Pines. Again, hope rekindled amongst us, although almost no one knew where this other island was and if the solution was temporary or definite. The only thing the Captain was able to learn that it was a small island some thirty-five miles wide, of exuberant vegetation, which was used partly as a penal colony.

Some immediately began to make plans with enthusiasm. They said that surely there was no synagogue, but that they would build it, that they would erect with their own hands the houses where they would live and the schools the children would attend. One of the passengers voiced out loud: "We'll show them that we are good people and that we will work hard and rise despite all circumstances."

Hours later, another cable from Mr. Meyer of the Joint Committee arrived. It informed us that the President had backed off from the idea of receiving us on the Isle of Pines because it had raised protests and a great opposition in Cuba. We could not understand how they were playing with us in such an atrocious manner.

The Captain and the Passengers' Committee sent two urgent cables to President Roosevelt, in which they asked for succor, but there was no reply. Meanwhile, messages to the President of Cuba continued, begging him to reconsider. They were also ignored.

On June 6th, one was received from the State Department of the United States, marked as urgent. It informed us that the procedure to apply for entry into the country was by waiting one's turn on the waiting list. Besides, it confirmed the refusal of accepting more Jews and ordered us to leave without further delay.



In the afternoon, another one arrived from the President of Cuba, with the final and irrevocable decision of not accepting us and considered the negotiations to have come to an end. He also informed us that the *Flandre* and the *Orduña* had already been turned back to Europe. With all that had happened we were certain that there would be no clemency for us. Then another cable was received from the HAPAG, with the indisputable order to return immediately to Europe. There didn't seem to be any other exit, everything had failed.

The *Saint Louis* got underway, en route back to Europe. We were on deck, in disbelief, disappointed, with our eyes fixed on North American land, which also moved away. We knew that the journey back to Germany brought us closer to a terrible fate and, in many instances, to death. How could everyone be so unfair? All we asked for was an opportunity to restart our lives, far from the horror that existed in our country.

We felt so humiliated! The Nazis seemed to be right: no one wanted us. Had the world shut its eyes so as not to realize the danger that we were in? I too closed mine, so as not to see how America faded in the distance and in my dreams.

Father had been tipped-off that several passengers were planning to highjack the ship. Very worried, he informed the Captain, who immediately called together a meeting to warn them that he would not back those who carried out criminal acts. He informed them that the Joint Committee and other organizations were in negotiations with some non-occupied European countries to admit us and that he would take it upon himself to do all that was in his power so that we would not be returned to Germany. He received a round of applause and a look of reprobation from the Nazi crew, who stormed out of the *Tanzplatz*. Once more, Schroeder had put himself in evidence in front of them and was obviously on our side.



On June 9th, Schroeder called his First Officer and father in an emergency meeting, of a confidential nature. He had learnt that Otto Schiendick, along with other Nazi crew members, was planning to level criminal charges against the passengers so that we'd be thrown in jail the moment we reached Germany.

He told them, too, of his secret plan, in case the Joint Committee negotiations failed. His intention was to sail the ship near Beachy Head, in the coast of Sussex in England, set fire to it and evacuate the passengers to dry land. He asked them both to keep it an absolute secret, to not even tell family members and much less the crew. The surprise element —he told them— was essential, especially since there were spies on board. Father told us about it sometime later.

That night Rachel and I were frightened to death. Again, we took refuge in mother and father's cabin in search of some emotional safety. We needed to believe that nothing bad could happen to us if we were together. I tried to play the violin for a while, but my fingers did not obey. I felt as if its sound had become muted, just like my spirits. When sleep finally overtook me, my nightmares were seasoned with a monodic motet, which seemed to have been composed in hell itself.



In the early morning another death took place on board. It was one of the ship's crew, a young German man who had been seen several times acting enthusiastically with a Jewish female passenger. Some said that he had been murdered by the Nazis because he had fallen in love with her, while others claimed it was a suicide. In that occasion no ceremony was held. They threw the body overboard before sunrise, without stopping or informing the rest.

On June 14$^{th}$, four weeks since our departure from Germany, already on our way back to Europe, the Joint Committee's negotiations bore fruit. Several urgent cables reached the *Saint Louis*: King Leopold II notified that Belgium would accept two hundred refugees, Queen Wilhelmina of The Netherlands one hundred and seventy-six, Great Britain three hundred and fifty, and France two hundred and fifty. The Captain gathered all the passengers to inform them about the news, which was received with a big round of applause.

By then, they began to ration the food, there was no bread or fruit and we were only given half a glass of water at every meal. The laundry ceased all operations. We no longer had clean towels or sheets, nor could our clothes be washed. It was expected that the fuel would only last us to reach the first European port.

The Captain ordered to redouble the vigilance. He was afraid there would be further suicides or a mutiny. People were exasperated. The Committee organized preventive rounds night and day. The rabbis conducted prayers services mornings and afternoons. Any unexpected turn of events would cause the operation to fail. Mother and father could not conceal their worries.

Each injustice eroded my faith a little more. Feeling furious with mankind, for being a Jew and for undergoing such a humiliating situation, I could not share in my parent's concern or knew how to cheer Rachel, who was very depressed. Surges of rage prevented me from sleeping at night. During the day, I walked obsessed along the ship's corridors, listening to other people's comments in case someone said something new. Mother and father bawled me out, but I was unable to avoid it.

One afternoon, I heard a girl ask her mother innocently: "Mother, if when we arrive in Europe we are thrown into a concentration camp, will they allow father to visit us?" Recalling Mr. Skolof's stories, I ran to hide in my cabin and cried for a long while. It was difficult not to let insanity take over, not to go crazy.

My only relief would have been to play the violin, but music became ever more dissonant, more diatonic. Notes would fail me, more elusive than ever. I was incapable of giving them shape. My fingers were inert, almost lifeless, like myself. I spent hours hugging my violin, wishing it would transmit some of its greatness, of its serenity.

On the morning of June 17th, we caught sight of the Belgium coast. Several officers from the Belgium government and the other countries that would take us in were waiting. They came up to us in two boats and boarded the *Saint Louis*. All the passengers were assembled in the Tanzplatz, where several tables were set up to process the documents. To the left for those who were going to France and England; to the right for those who disembarked in the Netherlands and Belgium.



In spite of asking each family in advance what was their country of choice, we had been warned that the final selection would be indisputable. Since mother was French, we asked to go to Paris, but were not certain to succeed. Some of her cousins lived there, but we weren't sure we'd be able to reach them because it had been some time since we had last heard from them. At least, we would be in familiar territory.

Some immigration and customs officials from the countries that would take us in boarded our ship. We greeted them with a round of applause. The Captain and the Committee supervised the entire procedure, always beneath Hitler's omnipresent portrait that we absolutely loathed. Mother was tearful, very pale and shook. I had never seen her thus. Father passed his arm around her shoulders, touched her and realized she was burning with fever. He asked me and Rachel to stay with her outside the hall. We placed a wet towel on her forehead and dried the tears that rolled down her cheeks irrepressibly.

At 2:30 PM, the *Saint Louis* docked in pier 18 of Antwerp, Belgium.

"How odd" —some said— "that after so much sailing and so many problems, we are hardly three hundred kilometers from Hamburg, where our accursed trip began."

Meanwhile, on port, the National Socialist Youth were carrying out a demonstration. The youngsters, many of them practically kids, wore brown shirts and a red band with the black swastika tied around an arm. They carried red flags with the Nazi insignia, and enormous portraits of Hitler. They hurled insults at us, such as: "Fucking Jews, why have you returned?" "Get out, pigs, we don't want you." The Belgium police quickly dispersed them, but we once again faced up to our undeniable reality. Fate, ever so uncertain and cruel, gave us a violent blow, casting us back to hell. I asked myself over and over, what is it we'd done to deserve so much hatred. Why were they insulting us in such manner?

Those who got off in Belgium would board an ugly, shabby-looking freight train, which waited next to the port. They left after lunch, amidst farewells and best wishes. We said goodbye from the deck, wishing them good luck.

On June 18th, at 9:30 AM and after breakfast, those headed to The Netherlands boarded the *Jan van Arckel*, a small ship that would take them to Rotterdam.

My friend Mark was lucky enough to be sent to Amsterdam, where he had relatives. We both knew we would never meet again. He approached me slowly, with tears in his eyes. We hugged and kissed. Rachel saw us and I asked her not to say anything. She winked at me and left, smiling.

The *Jan van Arckel* sailed off port escorted by several other boats from the Belgian police. Mark waived goodbye from his ship, until I lost sight of him.

On that same day, at 2 PM, the rest of us boarded the *Rhakotis*, a ship that dropped anchor next to the *Saint Louis* early that morning and which would take the groups headed to France and Great Britain. Each one received a small box with a sandwich and cookie for lunch, which we accompanied with a glass of water. In the *Saint Louis* only the crew remained. The Captain held his hand out to my father.



"Thank you, Dr. Felton. I don't know if we would've safely come this far without your invaluable help and equanimity," he said to him. Father was speechless, looked at the Captain, nodded, and shook his hand.

Afterwards he remained on deck for a long while, very serious, while we disembarked. His clear eyes were opaque; he looked sad and very tired. For a long while a playful cadenza amused itself in my head, while I meditated on how much we owed that man. We feared for his safety on his return to Germany. Having protected us would have terrible consequences for him. Deep within myself, I asked God to protect him so that nothing bad would happen to him. I broke up in tears when I said goodbye.

When we boarded the *Rhakotis*, we realized that the cabins wouldn't be sufficient for the six hundred of us who had come on board. Many were forced to sleep on the deck chairs in the outer passageways and in the salon sofas, but we were lucky enough to have a narrow cabin assigned to us, where all four of us settled in as best we could. Mother had recovered her customary composure and tried to cheer us up. I think she was excited to go to her homeland, above all, to Paris. "There are no Nazis there," she said smiling.

Dinner was frugal and we were still hungry. Clearly, the ship was not prepared for so many people, but we stuck together and kept alive. For the moment, that was sufficient and at least we were reassured not to be returning to Germany.

We left the port early the following morning. The *Rhakotis*' siren emitted its characteristic sound and the *Saint Louis* replied. The Captain and other crew members waved goodbye, but one of the Nazis shouted to us with derision, amidst the laughter of those around him: "Take advantage of the days of freedom you've got left, because in Dachau they're going to shave your beards off." I recalled with a shiver what Mr. Skolof had told us regarding his suffering in that place. An atonal low-pitched and frightful sound lingered in my mind for a while. I looked up at the sky that had become leaden and threatened with a storm.



All day long we sailed before the Belgium and French coastline, in the middle of thunder clap and copious rain. Night fell heavy, dark, and without stars or moon. The *Rhakotis* lurched in the storm and many were seasick. Father ran all over the place treating them, especially the elderly and children. Mother, Rachel and I helped him out. At least that kept us busy.

At 4:30 in the morning of June 20th, we reached the port of Boulogne-sur-Mer, where Mr. Franz Lambert awaited us, Secretary General of the French Agency for Refugees.

When he came on board and told us enthusiastically: "Welcome to free French territory," I felt an awkward incredulous happiness. A musical torrent of deafening percussions hijacked my reason. How much longer would France be a free territory? After what we'd gone through, we were convinced the Nazis were invincible. How long would they take to catch up with us? Would there be any safe place left for us to hide? I was scared, very scared, with an acute fear that someone might answer my questions. Nevertheless, I could not deny that we were happy, especially mother, for having reached France.

Two hundred and fifty passengers disembarked in Boulogne-sur-Mer. The rest continued that night on the *Rhakotis*, en route to Southampton, England. The porters refused to accept a tip for carrying our luggage. They bid us farewell with a smile, and wished us good luck.

That night we slept in a modest hotel, again the four of us in a single room. We talked for hours and made all sorts of plans, till we conked out. In spite of the worries that tormented us, for the first time in a long while we had piece of mind. A monodic cradle song lulled me, till I placidly fell asleep next to father.

Accompanied by Mr. Lambert, the following morning, we took a train to Le Mans. There he handed some money to each family and the groups split up. He made sure that ours, composed of thirty persons, took a train towards Paris. The others were headed to different destinations in the country's interior. We thanked him for his help and bid him farewell.

The train seats were wooden and the trip lasted five hours. We reached Paris absolutely exhausted. My sister and I had fond memories of the city and of our frequent visits to our maternal grandparents, deceased some years back. Out of reach from the Nazis, in France we felt safe.

In the train station we were received by an agent of Mr. Lambert's organization. He led the group to the office in the Rue Rivoli 204, to distribute them in different locations.

We were treated kindly and one of the employees went with us to a very old building not too far off, in a modest neighborhood but central. On our way there she apologized for the "inadequacy" of the lodging that they offered us.

The eight-story building didn't have an elevator. Our apartment was on the fifth floor, and was composed of barely a bedroom, a bathroom and a tiny dilapidated kitchen. The furniture was scarce: a square table, four chairs and an undefined colored sofa that, no doubt, had seen better days. The two beds were narrow, but we drew them together and made ourselves comfortable as best we could. Although the inevitable silent comparison with our home in Bremen was unavoidable, the truth of the matter was that we were very thankful to have a roof above our heads and for being together.

At the time, the country's economy was precarious. Every day more businesses closed and people wandered the streets aimlessly in search of work, whatever, as long as it would feed them. Our situation was desperate; the little money that we had left would soon run out.

A couple of weeks later, the French organization for the relief of refugees placed mother as a laborer in a uniform factory, a poorly paid job. It was harder for father, for people already feared employing Jews and, moreover, he did not have a license to practice medicine outside Germany. After several months of knocking on countless doors, of humiliating himself and begging, he found a job as a janitor in some pharmaceutical equipment department store. He accepted immediately, despite how degrading it was for him.

I was deeply saddened that mother would have to work for so many hours on her feet, and of seeing father return exhausted every afternoon, with dirty fingernails and fingers full of blisters. His delicate hands, which had the gift of healing others and saving lives, now submerged themselves in the floors' filthy waters. His medical instruments lay forgotten inside a suitcase in the bedroom.

Unable to find any traces of mother's cousins, we were able to enroll in school to continue our studies. Rachel assumed the new situation well, but I withdrew into my own world, clinging to my violin and to my goal of becoming a soloist, which moved farther and farther away. The internal melodies which had tormented me so much in the previous months ceased appearing.



We made friends with Fritz and Gertrude Bendowski, an elderly French-Jewish couple, owners of a nearby bakery. On the way out of school, my sister and I would help them clean the shop and with other chores in exchange for some foodstuff and bread. Fritz, serious and laconic, didn't communicate much with us, but Gertrude was a generous woman, of a singsong laughter, who welcomed us every afternoon with a pastry and a broad smile. She always compensated us with a little more than was our due. "For a job well done," she would say with a wink and a generous smile.

The following months elapsed in a fragile calmness. The threatening news followed disturbingly. Germany, in its inexorable advance, invaded Denmark, Norway, Belgium, Holland, Luxembourg and the North of Africa. The radio informed of measures ever more severe against the Jews in practically all European countries. And no one seemed to notice, as if it were better to ignore. What was happening to the world?

We wondered how much longer they would take to reach France, which by then had also declared war on Germany. In the first days of June, the radio announced the German army's ferocious attack, which advanced from Meuse. French surrender took place peacefully, and Paris was spared bombardment unlike other European cities. The Nazis entered triumphantly on June 14$^{th}$, 1940, with a monumental parade by the *panzerdivisionen* down the Champs-Élysées till the Arc de Triomphe de L'Étoile, amid the populations' stupor and sadness.

When we saw the French flags disappear from the flagpoles and replaced by the red ones with the black swastika that undulated defiantly in the city's most emblematic buildings, we understood that fate once again mocked us. Our most terrifying nightmares had turned into reality. The Nazis were finally here.

The leaders of the French government resigned and three days later, with Hitler's consent, Prime Minister Pétain took office and addressed the nation by radio, to ask the French to lay down their arms and to collaborate with the Germans. Shortly thereafter he signed an armistice treaty with Germany and Italy. France was left divided in two: the north under the absolute control of Hitler and the south in a so-called "free zone," which center would be the seaside resort town of Vichy with a collaborationist regime run by Pétain. Meanwhile, General de Gaulle set a government in exile, in the United Kingdom, from where he began the French Resistance movement.

What we knew so well started anew: the persecution of Jews, the beatings in the middle of the street, the mandate to wear a yellow star sewn on the chest, the forbiddance of entering public places, the injustice, the horror.

One morning on reaching the school where Rachel and I studied, we found signs of hate written in all the blackboards: "The Jews are our enemies, beware of them." The students didn't talk to us. That day the order was given that, hereafter, Jews could not attend learning centers. Again, we were obligated to stay home.



During those days numerous acts of burning books took place in the streets. They forced people to hand over the books they had of non-Arian authors. Bertolt Brecht, Alfred Kerr, Lion Feuchtwanger were all reduced to ashes, as well as the North American authors Jack London, Ernest Hemingway, Thomas Mann and many more. All that was not approved by the Nazis was considered "degenerate art" and had to be burnt, disappear. I wondered horrified if they'd do the same with the Jews.

Shortly thereafter father was laid-off. Mother, who was French of Christian origin, held on to her job, becoming the family's sole provider. Fritz and Gertrude were arrested and we never heard from them again. The bakery, like many other businesses, was shut down. We again became subhuman, once more we were worthless and it didn't seem to worry the world.

It was said that Hitler had given orders to destroy the city. People were scared and many wanted to flee. The roads were crammed, frequently bombarded and soldiers seemed to be everywhere. We tried leaving Paris, but immediately gave up. It was plain that, without transport or money, we wouldn't get very far.

The Nazis had set up the General Headquarters of their Paris Military Garrison next to our place, on the rue Rivoli 228, in the Hotel Meurice. The display of red flags with the swastika was impressive. The Place Vendôme, with its imposing obelisk in the middle, was full of soldiers. We were horrified by their proximity.



At the time our main concern was to pass unnoticed, hide, to dissolve ourselves in the great city. Father stayed with us in the apartment, while mother tried to hold on to her job. One day he told us with a serious face:

"Girls, if I were to go missing, promise me that you'll take care of mother. You are young and strong. No matter what happens, resist, fight to survive, no matter what. The war must come to an end someday. Promise me so."

I had never seen him so distressed. I felt so scared that what he asked of us would become a reality! Rachel stared at him blankly; she trembled and had become speechless. We looked for refuge in his lap, as when we were small. His protecting arms embraced us. We could not imagine what we'd go through, but his words and the memory of that moment would serve us as a beacon of strength in the coming times.

When I raised my head, in his tearful eyes there was an abyss of despair. There was no doubt that he was ready to give up his life for us. Unable to utter a single word, I only nodded my head and Rachel did likewise. Everything had been said. Our fragile word came asunder and it was our turn now to be the strong ones.

We were running very low on money. What mother earned hardly reached for a single meal a day. They turned off our heating because we were unable to pay for it and, when winter came, our apartment became an icebox. All four of us slept tightly together, beneath the only blanket we had, to keep warm, waiting the next day that will bring a few sun rays. Rachel had nightmares practically every night. Mother was skinny and pale. Father hardly spoke. I withdrew more and more.



Days were dense, with lesser and lesser hope. Events in France went from bad to worse. The collaborationist government installed in Vichy carried out the same atrocities as the Nazis. I was tormented by what father had asked of us, it turned in my head. Music no longer mattered and, little by little, I stopped practicing. My violin and my spirits lay gathering dust in a corner.

To keep her job, mother had to bear humiliations and the most denigrating conditions. She was married to a Jew, thus unworthy before the Nazis' eyes. She and father agreed that he would no longer try looking for work, since the situation for Jews became ever more difficult. We had become lepers; people despised us.

Father devoted his time to teach Rachel and me so that we not fall behind in our studies. "So that when everything returns to normal," he would tell us. For more than a year we lived in a most precarious fashion. Spirits were running high, it was teeming with soldiers and the risk of being apprehended was very great. We hardly set foot on the street so as not to be seen, but knew the Nazis' reach was inexorable and that, sooner or later, we'd be hunted like hares.

On the July 16th, the Grande Raffle took place in which thousands of Jews were captured on the streets and in their homes. Neighbors arrived agitated with news of beatings and massive arrests. The noise coming from the street, the screams, the sound of soldiers' boots, the rush of vehicles, the screeching sound of brakes, all attested to what was occurring.

As we feared, mother did not return at her usual time. We were frightened to death to think that she might be among the detainees. We didn't know what to do or where to go to look for her. Father did not dare leave us by ourselves, in case we might be captured. All night long our eyes were fixed on the clock that, due to some kind of sortilege, turned the minutes into hours. Suspended by some fragile thread of hope, we prayed that it all be a terrible nightmare and that mother open the door any minute.

None of us could sleep. Dawn caught father sitting on the edge of the bed with a fixed stare lost in some nonexistent point. Rachel cried non-stop. My arid eyes refused to weep; my body trembled and I felt as if I were going to pass out. I thought that all three of us would go mad. I tried to keep calm, comfort them both, myself, but was unable. Terror froze me, took hold of my senses. A deaf scream traveled throughout my bowels, uncontrollable, about to explode in my bosom. Something not melodic, like a dissonant pounding of kettledrums, cymbals and drums, struck *in crescendo* in my head.

That afternoon we were shaken by what we'd feared for so long: the screeching of the military vehicles' breaks and the unmistakable echo of the soldiers' boots rushing up the stairs. Dry knocks reverberated in each of the building's doors, where lots of us Jews lived. Father had to open the door. Soldiers burst into our dwelling and ordered us with shouts to come out immediately, while pointing at us with their weapons. My first reaction was to grab my violin. I was afraid they'd take it away from me, but in the moment's confusion, they didn't notice. We stormed out in the middle of all the pushing and shoving from those men.

The trucks to carry the detainees were stationed in front of the building. A soldier, dressed in an impeccable uniform and shiny boots, directed the operation with an amazing calmness. Standing in the middle of the street —with his legs apart, his hands on his hips and a whip in his right hand— he smilingly approved how his subordinates, with insults and rifle butt blows, abused that bunch of helpless human beings who were scared to death.



Soldiers pushed the children, grabbed them by an arm, by the clothing, by the hair and flung them into the truck, while they laughed and made cruel jokes. The passersby who witnessed the spectacle cheered them on to ingratiate themselves with them, applauded and hurled insults against the Jews. Only two women dared confront the soldiers to try and stop them and defend the children, but they too were thrown into the truck. What was happening to humanity? What had we turned into?

We were transferred to the SS barracks for interrogation. The wailing and screams from our traveling companions was bone-chilling. Frightful and after seeing the callousness and cruelty of those men, there was no doubt they were going to murder us upon reaching our destination.

For several days, we were crowded together in some prison cells of the *Comissariat Général aux Questions Juives* with hundreds of unknown persons, whose crime seemed to be the same as ours. They hardly gave us food or water. We only had two lavatories, overflowing with excrement, and the stench was unbearable.

The beatings were constant. Luckily, they didn't separate us from father who often told us: "We must resist, we cannot allow them to intimidate us." But the reality was that Rachel and I were scared to death. I am sure he too. I clung to my violin and tried hiding it from the guards. I was surprised that they hadn't taken it away from me.

We secretly hoped of finding mother, comforting ourselves by thinking that perhaps she had hidden somewhere. Overwhelmed by a strange mixture of relief and fear, we looked everywhere in case we got a glimpse of her.

Some days later, we were again thrust inside some trucks and taken to the train station, without being told where they were sending us. All three of us desperately looked at the faces of that human crowd which they forced onto the carriages. Almost in unison, we made out a familiar silhouette on the platform: a ragged woman, round-shouldered, who dragged her feet awkwardly. I recognized her profile and her auburn hair. I hesitated. That woman looked like a beggar, an old woman; it couldn't be her.

"Mother!" I called out.

"Vera!" father screamed.

She turned her head very slowly. Her former blue eyes had lost their color and sank into deep black shadows. In her aqueous stare was reflected a maze of nightmares. She had a hematoma on her right cheekbone and a wound on her forehead, with coagulated blood. Father moved forward, we all three ran towards her and hugged her with tears in our eyes. She hardly reacted, as if she didn't recognize us. The soldiers yelled at us and drove us along with the butts of their weapons, to walk quicker. Others brought their menacing dogs close.

They forced us on to some freight train for cattle transport, without seating, the windows boarded with coarse wooden planks. In each carriage, some nine meters long, hundreds of people piled up. They closed the sliding doors with force, making a loud noise. People screamed desperately. Where were they taking us?

We managed to settle in a corner and brought mother close to some small gaps in-between the window boards, so that she could breathe some fresh air. Father held her tight and examined her wounds, while my sister and I looked upon them sadly. I held on to my violin as a salvation board. I had managed thus far for them not to take it away from me. Father's words hammered in my head, along with a *kyrie*, a terrifying background melody that stayed with me for practically the entire journey. We had to survive, no matter what the cost.

The train got under way and the screams became deafening. Since the carriage was full, with the lurches it was impossible to remain standing, but neither was there space to sit down. We tried to keep an emotional and physical balance. The heat was suffocating; hardly any air penetrated. Weakened from hunger, thirst and the blows received, we wore an interrogation sign in our eyes without understanding the justification to that ghastly nightmare. I beheld in horror what was happening to our family and our people.

Several hours later, the floor was covered in a sticky mixture of urine, excrement and vomit, more so after a bucket had spilt that the Nazis had left there for us to relieve ourselves, as if we were animals. Since practically no fresh air penetrated the carriage, the stench crept into our noses and mouths, producing irrepressible nausea. In our carriage, a pregnant woman vomited uncontrollably and three elderly people died from asphyxia. Several people laid down unconscious and the children cried desperately.

We had no idea where they were taking us until many hours later, in-between the cracks we started seeing signs in an unknown language. A couple said it was Polish. Soon thereafter, several signs informed us that we were approaching a place called Oswiecim. That is how we learned that we'd crossed Germany and were in Poland, occupied by the Nazis since 1939. It didn't bode well.

In the carriage, a man mentioned that he'd been told that there were several labor camps in Poland and that Auschwitz was considered the most terrible of them all. It was the first time we heard that name, but I recalled what Mr. Skolof had told us about his horrific experience in Dachau. A cold and unrestrained tremor traveled throughout my body. I looked at my parents and sister. All four of us were petrified by fear. We neared hell and there was nothing we could do to prevent it.

A little later the train stopped abruptly, and we fell to the ground unable to avoid it. Again, the doors opened with a great racket. The Nazi soldiers received us with yells and a string of insults. *Alle heraus*! Everyone out! With shoves, they immediately ordered us out. That atrocious trip had taken fourteen hours.

Families could not touch their dead nor succor those who had passed out or were very weak. Those who could not get out of the carriages on their own legs, the soldiers would execute them right there, in between laughter and derogatory comments.

*Alles dort lassen!* Leave all your belongings here! They repeatedly yelled at us so that we take our suitcases and place them on the platform. They said we could pick them up later in a warehouse they called Kanada. I grabbed my violin, but a soldier snatched it away from me and flung it onto the carriage floor, on the filth, and asked me sarcastically if I intended to give the dead a concert. A part of me was ripped out. That instrument was the only connection that I had left with my own life, with sanity.

Our vision was blurry, our lips sandy and swollen. Thirst scorched our throats and hunger stung our bowels. We had nothing to drink or eat in more than twenty-four hours. We were exhausted, weak, frightened, but that didn't matter to them. They threatened us by bringing their ferocious dogs up close, which seemed ready to attacks us. We had to walk quickly, even if we were sick, it didn't matter if it were an old man, a woman, or a child. If someone fell, they struck him so that he'd get up. If not, they'd kill him on the spot with a bullet.

Mother and father seemed to have aged years in those last hours. Rachel, with an immense tenderness, smiled to mother. I did the same with father and told him very gently: "Remember that we have to be strong, we must survive. We are together and that is what matters." He nodded with a faint smile, without uttering a word, but with infinite sadness reflected on his face. A soldier pushed us with violence and we fell to the ground.

No one told us where we were and why had they taken us there. What was plain was that those people didn't tolerate weakness or disobedience. Father supported mother with strength, helping her walk. Rachel shook with fear; I was afraid she'd faint. At that moment, realizing how much I loved my sister, I took her by the hand and told her. It might have been too late to tell her afterwards.

I treaded heavily and tried to hold my tears back for the loss of my violin, for the humiliations we had to endure, for everything they forcefully took from us. I was certain that we had reached hell and that at the end of the road death awaited.

In a terrifying scene, thousands of tattered and smelly people, half dead or alive, marched dragging our feet along a dusty path which seemed to us never-ending. Suddenly, we were before and imposing iron-gate. In its topmost wrought iron arch could be read the following inscription: "*Arbeit macht frei*" – "Work will make you free."

I was horrified, as I felt as the music return all at once in my head, in torrents, in hasty chords. It was the *Totentanz*, the Dance of the Dead.

Someone yelled:

"We are in Auschwitz!"

## Second Movement – *Andante impetuoso*

Alex's silhouette was reflected against the semi-dark room. Standing before the two coffins, the voices of the departed hammered in his head, farther and farther away. A young woman had just entered and looked at him from a distance. "How different from the Alex I know. It must be the transformation that emerges after the suffering. The virtuoso that fills the great music halls, the pampered of all the world's audiences, the one who seems not to need anything or anyone, now is nothing but a man battered by death," she thought. She stood there motionless, engrossed in her own thoughts. She didn't want to interrupt the distressing dialogue, imperceptible, that the man seemed to be carrying out with his memories.

People started to arrive. Armand came in hastily and hugged the woman, his sister. They approached Alex who had not noticed their presence.

"Mariana, I was sure you'd come!" He exclaimed with sadness, while he melted with her into one long embrace.

"I could not be absent, you know how much I loved them," she said.

"I know."

"How could this have happened? It's so terrible..."

"We spoke two days ago, as was customary before my concerts. We joked and made plans to meet up in Paris. If only had I known it was going to be the last time I was to hear their voice! I am devastated, I can't believe it."



Mariana didn't know what to answer. The sudden death of Henry and Amalia had taken everyone by surprise. The couple adored their only son and considered her part of the family, despite the divorce.

"How life changes in a blink," Alex thought. Uncle Leo's call two nights ago, shortly before the Carnegie Hall concert, with the news of the accident. He didn't know how he'd been able to play *Petrushka*, and neither could he remember the encore he offered in response to the audiences' applause, only the painful need to leave the stage and be alone to demand God an answer.

As soon as the concert was over, he and Armand quickly headed for the airport. By then they had further details of what had occurred: "an accident, a truck hit them head on and they died instantly," Armand told him.

They hardly spoke during the flight. Alex pretended to be asleep, he didn't feel like talking, but the images haunted him. He recalled the happy moments when his parents traveled to meet up with him, his mother's humorous wit, and his father's wisdom. They would sit in the concert hall's front row and he was thrilled to see them there, proud of his successes. Then they would return to their home on the island and he'd continue with his itinerary, with his secretary and great friend Armand, from city to city, from country to country.

Alex sank into a horrible emptiness, in an absurd silence devoid of laughter or music. Their countenances became blurry. He had lost them forever.

The plane was about to land in Puerto Rico. Alex caught sight of the beaches and the lovely tropical landscape. Even in his Paris apartment, where he felt so comfortable, Alex was unable to avoid missing his mother's country, that beloved island where he grew up and where his roots were. He felt an acute pain facing the fact that his parents wouldn't be there.



***

The Methodist priest conducted the funeral services at the church the Yorks attended. Relatives, friends, journalists, government officials and the cream of the crop of the musical world had gathered in solidarity with the pianist. In the first row, Javier and Alicia, Armand's parents and Mariana, the Yorks' best friends, their neighbors and regular traveling companions. Sadness and incredulity could be read on their faces.

Alex remained crestfallen during the entire ceremony while his uncle Leo, his mother's only brother and as the family's representative, addressed the assistants. In turn and eager for that procession to come to an end, with barely an audible voice and with infinite sadness, Alex thanked everyone for their condolences.

Armand and Mariana accompanied him to the old family house, full of memories, in which every nook and corner had its own anecdote to tell. In the middle of the drawing room, his old grand piano now waited for him, which Amalia always had tuned when she knew her son was coming. In that occasion, it was out of tune, voiceless, like Alex.

"Do you remember how father was always against my studying music? He wanted me to be an engineer, like himself. At first, he said pianists were always starving," Alex mused, addressing himself to Armand, with nostalgia and half a smile.



"It took your mother lots of persuasion to convince him, but Henry finally yielded when he realized your talent and determination. In the end, when he saw your triumph, he became your greatest admirer," Armand remarked, who felt a profound affection for Alex's father, whom he considered a friend, despite the age difference.

"What are you going to do with the house?" Mariana asked, as if she wanted to change the conversation to more tangible subject matters.

"Leave it to Uncle Leo. After all, the house once belonged to his parents. He and mother grew up here. It's very big and wouldn't make sense to maintain. However, I'd like to buy an apartment in San Juan. Coming here as much my schedule allows is a treat and hence would prefer not to lose contact with the island. I disconnect from everything whenever I spend time here. Let me call Philip, father's lawyer, so that he tells how best to proceed."

"There are lots of papers in this cabinet," Mariana remarked, while looking through the drawers that Alex had just finished opening.

"From what I see, we have lots of work. Everything must be sorted out. Ah, by the way, when Pollot called the funeral home to convey his condolences, he reconfirmed the details of the Paris concert next month. He said he'd call again to arrange some details regarding the Berlin and Prague concerts. Luckily, you have the piano right here, so I will call for it to be tuned. You make sure to practice, and I'll take care of the rest," Armand said.



"As usual, my dear friend, as usual," Alex assented.

"If you wish, I can help. I am on holiday and will be going to stay on the island for the entire summer," Mariana remarked.

"By all means, Mariana, I am very grateful. Your help will be very useful," Alex answered.

Since their divorce five years ago, Alex hadn't seen her. "She must be thirty-five. She's become a very interesting-looking woman, with another air, surer of herself, and has a sparkle in the eye that I couldn't recall," Alex thought. He further admired Mariana's stylized profile and her long chestnut-color hair that once upon a time he liked so much. Alex beheld her absorbed in his own thoughts.

Sadness did not abandon him. He sat at the piano, but this one did not give forth its habitual phrasing either, but rather a melody of confusing timbres, as if the notes leapt off the score, without him being able to recover them. He closed the keyboard and left the house in a rush, with no fixed destination in mind.

After walking for a while to the rhythm of his heart's syncopated beats, Alex sat in one of the benches in the Miramar Park where his parents used to take him to when he was a child. He looked for cover beneath the immense trees which had lavished him with shelter and shade during his childhood. Mariana had followed him and sat by his side. They looked at each other in silence.



"I always ask Armand about you. I know you live in Miami."

"Yes, I teach German at the university."

"Are you happy?"

"I can't complain."

"You haven't remarried…" Alex remarked.

"Neither have you."

"Do you think anyone would want to run behind me all over the world?"

"I was once willing…"

"Let us return home, it's getting late," he answered, offering her his hand to rise from the bench, while he questioned her with his eyes.

***

"Music is a most wonderful exercise that heals the deepest wounds," Armand said in a low voice to his sister, while they sorted out some papers and listened to the melodies that came from the piano.

"He practices a minimum of eight hours a day and he obviously enjoys it. It has always been so," Mariana answered.

"You still love him, right?"

"I don't know, Armand, the divorce was very painful. I don't want to talk about it," she said emphatically.

The melodies ceased. Alex had taken a break and was coming towards them. He sat in one of the armchairs and began to inspect one of his mother's drawers: the lock of his first haircut, messages with childish drawings, his school grades, photos, his concert programs, and newspaper clippings. His entire life encapsulated in that space, everything organized by her with devotion, with love, as if they were real treasures. He closed the drawer, deeply moved by the memories.

An expert had to be called in to open the safe deposit box, as Alex didn't know the combination. "It's curious how we don't prepare for death," he reflected sadly.

All three of them became immersed in a thorough examination of the documents they found inside: bonds, savings certificates, investments, title deeds, a will and other miscellany.

"Alex, look at this!" Armand exclaimed.

"What is it?"

"This document looks old and is in another language. I think it's German."

"Translate it, Mariana, please," Alex said.

"Hand it over," Mariana said, who carefully examined the hand-written piece of yellowish paper.

"What does it say?"

"It seems to be something regarding an adoption. It is forty years old. Who was adopted in your family?"

"I have no idea, my parents never told me about anyone being adopted. What else does it say?"

"That it took place in Münich, Germany, in February of 1945, that it had to be registered before the U.S. authorities and that the adopter was Henry York. Further below it states that it was a boy. It's quite blurry and somewhat torn on the folds. There are parts which are illegible."

"Father adopted someone? How strange! It must have been while he was in the army."

"In 1945 the war had just ended... Your father was in Europe, right?" Armand said.

"Yes, although he didn't like talking about it. It seems that it was something rather traumatic. Every time I asked him, father always answered that it had been such a terrible time in his life that it was better to forget about it. He was very young back then."

"Ask your Uncle Leo, I am sure he knows something. That child would have been raised with you, for he'd be your age more or less. How strange your parents never mentioned it. Could he have died?" Mariana asked.

"Could the adoptee be me?"

An uncomfortable silence fell over the room. Alex considered how little he looked like his parents. The afternoon's thick semidarkness enveloped them.

Thoughtful, Alex returned to the piano, without turning the light on. Before, he found the answers easily in the music, but on this occasion it seemed intent on following a different melodic line. He closed his eyes and conjured his mother's image sitting in the armchair before him.

He had nightmares that night. The image of an unknown child appeared to him, spreading his arms, calling him. When he was able to see his countenance, it was his very own face he saw. He awoke drenched in sweat and all shaken. As soon as it dawned he went to see his uncle.

"Did you say an adoption? I have no idea."

"My parents told me I was born in Washington, DC. Were you there? Do you remember that?"



"I too was in the military at that time, but in Italy. After the war was over and upon my return to Puerto Rico, you guys had just finished moving to the island. You were almost two years old when I met you for the first time."

"What happened to that kid, who was he? Someone in the family must know something? Could it be me?"

"I don't think so. You know I'm your mother's only brother, your only family. Your paternal grandparents and your father's only sister died before you were born. Besides, my sister wouldn't have hidden something so important from me. How strange! What do you plan on doing?"

"This is all very confusing… not quite sure what to think of. But I am going to find out the truth and get to the bottom of this. That boy came out of nowhere and we don't know where he is or what happened to him. The worst thing is that the only ones who had the answer are no longer alive."

That same afternoon, Alex told Mariana what his uncle had told him.

"Don't you find it strange? I also asked my parents, but they are as intrigued as we are. They were very good friends and it is strange that your parents never told my parents something that important. It's a mystery."

"Like a riddle… It appears that the adoption took place in Germany so many years back, that I am not sure that it'll be possible get to the truth. Just wish I had the time to find out, but I must fulfill my concert obligations. I can't cancel."

"Let me carry out the investigative work, Alex. I've just begun my holiday and I had thought about staying in Puerto Rico, but I can change my plans. I am not accountable to anyone. What do you say?"

"Are you sure? It would be wonderful. Plus, you speak several languages, which is very convenient. Only on one condition: that you let me cover all the expenses that you incur and that I allocate an amount for your services. It wouldn't be fair otherwise."

"Very well..."

"Perhaps you'll have to travel to Germany or to some other country behind the Iron Curtain; it's possible that you'll have difficulty with the visas and some permits. This can be complicated."

"We shall see, but if I don't achieve something conclusive in the allotted time, you will have to hire someone else."

"It's a deal, then. But you must promise me you'll be very careful with your research. I'm so grateful to you! You have no idea…"

That very afternoon Mariana started making phone calls to Germany. No one seemed to know where she could find the information she required. The document had been issued in Münich, but it was not clear what agency had been responsible for the adoption. She realized she wouldn't achieve much more over the telephone, so decided on traveling to Münich to start from there. Perhaps in person she could obtain something more specific and quicker.

During several weeks, Alex and Armand classified documents, packed photos, family mementos and vacated the house so that Uncle Leo and his wife could move in. Alex decided to keep some pieces of furniture, paintings, and, of course, his piano. He bought an apartment next to the beach, from which terrace he could look out onto the sea. "This spectacle only takes place in the Caribbean," he thought.



Even though Alex kept up with his daily practice routine, his mind was in a perennial struggle. The adopted child crossed the threshold of reality, to again hide in-between the shadows. "Where are you? Who are you? Am I the adopted one? Me…?" he thought.

Mariana called several times from Münich to give him an update of what she had achieved so far. The office which had issued the certificate no longer existed. Caught between the bureaucracy and carelessness, she was being sent from one agency to another, and was wasting lots of time. She had been running around for three weeks, her efforts bore no fruit and she was becoming frustrated, until Alex received a phone call.

"Alex, we finally have a good lead! I was told to visit the office of the International Red Cross. After spending several days there, they helped me obtain some trustworthy information regarding the agency that handled the adoptions of the 'boys of the war children.' That's how they're called. Years ago, those records were sent to Hamburg, where I am off to this very afternoon. If something transpires from my search, I'll let you know."

"Awesome. I am off to Paris to play since I am unable to cancel it, and told Armand to cancel the Prague and Berlin concerts."

"Pollot is going to hit the ceiling…"

"I don't care. Tomorrow we're off to Paris. After the concert, I'll immediately fly to Hamburg to help you with the investigation and to be present when you discover something. This uncertainty is killing me: I can hardly sleep and have nightmares every night."

"This is harder than I expected. I too have an enormous curiosity to know the truth. Remember the Hotel Junt in Hamburg? I made reservations there. Call me when you get in."

He remained pensive, with the telephone receiver in his hand. The memory of Mariana exacerbated his senses. How wrong he had been to think that her image would disappear with time and distance! In all these years of loneliness since the divorce, Alex never met anyone like her. Would it be possible that he'd be so blind? His mother adored Mariana, like the daughter she never had. It seemed as if, from that new dimension she was now in, she had again sent her to his side when he needed her the most. In short, at forty he had no family of his own. He had never felt so alone.

The Red Cross had set up an appointment for Mariana with Mr. Marc Fietze, Director of the Adoptions Registry of Hamburg. With every new step she took grew the fear of what she would discover. She was certain that the truth, no matter what it was, was going to be very painful for Alex.

Mariana slept very poorly that night and woke up at dawn. The hotel was hardly a block away from Feldstrasse 61, where the Registry's office was located, so she decided to walk there. She arrived a little before nine, the appointed hour.

Fietze was lean and short, with sparse hair and a bushy mustache. His unexpressive face made Mariana think that she was before another failure. The man indicated for her to take a seat, and she handed him the document, along with the power of attorney in which Alex authorized her to carry out the investigation.

"Mr. Alex York, whom I represent, is the son of Mr. Henry York, recently deceased. He was an American citizen and, as part of the United States Army, was stationed in Germany during the Second World War. As you can see from the document I have just handed you, it would seem that he adopted a boy. His son Alex has just found out. He needs to know the details, who that person is and where could he locate him."

The civil servant examined the piece of paper thoroughly, placed it under a magnifying glass and said with concern:

"This document is very old. I fear it will be very difficult to find further information. We usually come upon lots of inaccuracies in these cases because, at that time, given the reigning chaos and the urgency to help orphaned children, matters concerning adoptions were not always properly registered. I am going to assign an investigation, but I can't promise anything. Perhaps in a couple of days we'll have something. Where can I locate you?"

"I'm staying very close by, at the Hotel Junt, room 316. I'm planning to remain in Hamburg for several more days, waiting for your news. For whatever you can do, I am very grateful."

Mariana left hopeful. After all, Mr. Fietze showed a genuine desire to help her. Perhaps by the time Alex arrived, she'd have something more concrete.

She took advantage to explore the city that, much to her surprise, turned out to be very beautiful. Two rivers cut across it and people move from one place to another by boat. The port's activity was frenetic, with cranes and stevedores all over the place. The gray and oily water beat against the ships, whose sirens intermingled with the seagull's shrieks, flying in flocks. In the air the smell of the sea's brine mixed with the aromas of spices and coffee.

After many days of tension, Mariana felt exhausted. She had dinner in one of the restaurants in the area and returned to the hotel early, when a mantle of mist began to shroud everything.

***

Paris' Théâtre du Châtelet was packed. Alex played Rachmaninoff's Piano Concerto No. 3: three movements of pure virtuosity. He performed the first, *Allegro ma non tanto*, diatonic and savage, followed by a *cadenza*. The *Adagio* of the second movement hypnotized the audience. And the third, the *Finale*, with its passionate melody and the characteristic four-note rhythm considered as the composer's signature, brought the frenzied audience to its feet in a standing ovation. He gave a gentle *encore*, Chopin's "Minute Waltz." A triumphant night!

Armand watched from behind the scenes the same performance he had lived over and over, throughout the years.

He wondered how Alex could play given the suffering he was going through. He loved him like a brother.

Alex woke up late the following morning. His apartment on the *Avenue Foch* was immense. In the middle of the drawing room stood out the Steinway concert piano and, as only piece of furniture, an enormous white leather modular sofa, a reclining armchair and a little table in a corner. He threw open the terrace windows, from where the city's sunbathed rooftops could be seen. He closed his eyes and recalled with yearning that he would soon see Mariana. Armand came in euphoric with the daily papers, *Le Monde*, *Le Figaro*, *Le Parisien*, and placed them on the table. "Here you go," he said smiling. "The usual: 'York exceeds himself.' 'The virtuoso Alex York once again demonstrates why he is considered one of the best pianists in the world.' 'Brilliant concert by Maestro York,'" he read out loud.

At the moment, Alex cared little for the reviews. That ghost coming out of the past chased him, tormented him, and he was unable to get it out of his head. The ghost could not be put to rest until he deciphered the mystery that up until recently had taken ownership of his life.

"I am leaving for Hamburg in three days to catch up with your sister; to take the time that is needed to resolve this mystery that is driving me crazy. What are you planning on doing?"

"Return to Puerto Rico to rest, especially after listening to Pollot's furious screams when I told him you were canceling the Berlin and Prague concerts. Never had I seen him so upset."

"He'll get over it. Pollot is a little neurotic, but must respect my decision. Never before had I canceled a concert on him. For the first time in my entire career, last night I did not enjoy my execution. The technique was fine, but not the feeling and that does not satisfy me. I have to pull myself and my life together in order to go on."

"It's because you're under enormous pressure. It's understandable."

"You know what? I love your sister."

"That's old news."

"I was a total idiot. Our marriage failed because of me. I was so centered on my career... That is why I lost her and she no longer wants to have anything to do with me."

"Now I am really convinced that you're blind. My friend, my sister is crazy about you, she never ceased to be. Don't you realize it?"

"You think so? It had been so long since I had seen her! I feel she's someone else, distant."

"What did you want? That after all that happened, that she run into your arms? Speak to her, Alex. Your career is consolidated. What else do you want to achieve? Don't waste any more time, you're still young. It's time you create a family. Until when are you going to put it off?"

"I feel alone, as if my life has no direction."

"Totally understand. I wish I could stay planted in one single place too, marry, and have kids. We're behaving like two hermits. Very cultured, true, but we're like two prairie wolves. People must think we're homosexuals," Armand added with a loud laugh.

“You often speak to the Puerto Rico Symphony Orchestra cellist, the one you recently met…”

“Her name is America. That woman drives me crazy! When we first met, I immediately invited her for dinner and afterwards called her on several occasions. She likes me… for sure. We’ll see each other the minute I set foot in San Juan. Alex, I think I’m in love.”



The telephone ring interrupted them. It was Mariana.

“Hello Alex, how did your concert go last night? I imagine a success, as usual.”

“We were just going over the papers. The critics treated me kindly, but I don’t know how I managed. My head is elsewhere. Do you know what the encore was?” Alex asked her.

“Chopin’s waltz I like so much?”

“Yes, that one, I hadn’t played till last night. And I thought about you.”

“…”

“How is the investigation coming along? Are you in Hamburg?”

“There is something I have to tell you. The Director of the Adoptions Registry has just finished giving me a most interesting report. It confirms that indeed your father adopted a boy in 1945, like the document that you found states. Do you want to hear where he came out of? From Auschwitz...”

“Do you mean Auschwitz, the concentration camp?”

“That’s right, the one that was in Poland. He was barely a baby when the camp was liberated and, apparently, they took him to Münich, where the adoption took place.”

"Who took him to Münich?"

"It's not known, only that he showed up there."

"Do you know why my father adopted him? Did he take him back to the United States? Who was the kid? Who were the parents?"

"Wait... I still don't have all the details. The report doesn't mention that. At least we know where the child came from. Now we must find out the rest and what happened to him."



"How do you plan to do that?"

"Mr. Fietze recommends that I travel to Poland, since his office cannot provide me with further information. He was kind enough to coordinate with the Red Cross so that they help me with the entry permits. Not an easy task, as we very well know. In addition, I called the Center's Director that is now in Auschwitz, requesting his help. He also told me that, being your father an American, he must've registered the adoption in the U.S. But I will take care of that later."

"It seems that you are starting to unveil the mystery."

"Tomorrow morning, I am flying to Krakow to see what I can find out in Auschwitz. I was feeling quite frustrated, but now it gives me the chills to have to go to that place."

"I'll be there on Friday. I'm not foreseeing any problems in entering Poland, since I performed in Warsaw a couple of months ago and luckily my visa has not expired. Where will you be staying?"

"I made a reservation at the Chopin Hotel."

"Music shadows me… I will call you the moment I get there. Thanks, Mariana. I really appreciate everything you're doing for me."

Alex, doleful, let himself collapse on the armchair. He tried in vain to find the answers. Why didn't his father tell him that he had adopted a child? Did his mother know? Why did they remain silent? Where was this person now? Did he die? Could it be possible that he'd be the adoptee? Alex discarded the idea, but it kept coming back into his brain, once more: "Could it be me?" He felt afraid, very afraid.



***

The Red Cross had enabled Mariana a permit from the Soviet authorities to rent a car so she could travel to the outskirts of the city. On the following day, she headed towards Auschwitz, approximately an hour away from the city. While driving through the Polish countryside and admiring the bucolic and serene landscape, with houses that displayed gardens full of flowers, she wondered how it was possible that in the proximity of such a pleasant place an inexplicable abomination of such magnitude could have taken place.

Mr. Alfred Rosenback, the Center's Director, was waiting for her. He explained to her that Auschwitz was an enclave of three main camps and several dozen satellite camps. He was on his way to the city to take care of some important business but promised that he'd take her on a tour of the camp when Alex arrived. Meanwhile, he assigned Nora Goldsmith, the Archives' custodian, to assist her.

Nora was a serious and efficient Polish woman, big and coarse, about sixty years old, who spoke several languages fluently and seemed to know by heart the cluster of classified folios arranged throughout several rooms. The cold walls, very white, of that immense enclosure hid thousands of terrifying stories. Mariana didn't know where to begin, but Nora turned out to be a very valuable resource.

"During the war, thousands of children were sent to this place. Many were killed upon arrival and those that were spared either were experimented upon, or were made to work like adults. The majority died of malnutrition or from illnesses. If pregnant women arrived, they were immediately sent to the gas chambers because the Nazis considered them unable to work and a nuisance. Sometimes they waited for the baby's birth so they could kill it. There were instances when the mother, with her child in her arms, died in the gas chambers."



"Did the Soviets find any newborns when they arrived in Auschwitz?"

"Those that were born right before the camp's liberation had more chances of survival because the Nazis were busy at other things and were already aware that they'd lose the war," Nora explained to her.

Mariana noticed that, beneath her blouse's sleeve, some numbers stuck out tattooed on the woman's left forearm. "Behind her mild appearance must lie, well hidden, her story," she thought.

Nora intuited what Mariana was thinking and said:

"You noticed the numbers on my arm… I too was here, in Auschwitz, almost two years, till liberation in January of 1945, when the Soviets entered," she told her, while she rolled the sleeve of her left arm.

"And you stayed after the war?" Mariana asked Nora, slightly embarrassed for making her reveal her secret.

"No, first I went to Warsaw, my native city, but felt unhappy because I'd lost my entire family. Besides, anti-Semitism had not disappeared altogether, as if the Nazi sympathizers had not understood that the war had ended. I considered going to Palestine, but the English intercepted the boats and sent the refugees to detention camps in Cypress."

"Didn't you think of going to the United States?"

"Yes, but the quota for immigrants was limited."

"Didn't you try any other country in Europe?"

"Many European countries had closed their borders before the fear of a refugee invasion. It was then I decided to move to Krakow where I had some cousins. When this Center was created, I applied for the position of Director of the Archives and was immediately hired. There was lots of documentation, but it was in total disarray. I accepted, perhaps in an effort to make sense of everything that happened and, especially, to help all those who'd lost track of their loved ones. It was a hard and pressing task because people needed to know what happened to their families. I could not tell a mother, a husband, a son… to come back later. They needed an answer and we did our best to give it to them as soon as possible."

"It must have been a terrible experience," Mariana remarked.

"Unless one has lived it, it is impossible to imagine and much less to understand. Throughout all these years, I have seen situations similar to the one you present us with. I will do everything possible to help you."

During the following two days, Mariana was immersed in various documents that Nora furnished her, especially those that referred to the children born in Auschwitz.

Friday afternoon, when Mariana reached her hotel, she found Alex who had just arrived in Poland and had already checked in. They met for dinner. Mariana looked haggard and it was obvious that she was very tired.



"I am devastated. Did you know that the Nazis had the morbid obsession to thoroughly record all their atrocities, even with photos and films? What took place during the Second World War was a conspiracy against humanity. The Archives are full of reports of torture, genetic manipulations and unbelievably ghastly medical experiments. They would perform surgery on people without anesthesia, burn their organs with acid, subject them to extreme temperatures, and mutilate them. Not only did they use men as guinea pigs, but also women and children, even the newborns."

"How dreadful!", Alex exclaimed.

"I have read terrible accounts. On several occasions I was forced to leave the room, with nausea, with a knot in the stomach, with a blurred vision. Poor people, how much they must've suffered!"

Alex listened to her, very serious and in silence. Mariana went on:

"Even though the Center's Director is going to take us to tour the camp, I felt very curious to see some additional sites and yesterday I asked Nora, in charge of the Archives, to accompany me on a small tour. I went into one of the gas chambers and thought I could hear the prisoners' screams, feel their anguish. Imagine what it must have been like to see oneself nude among hundreds of strangers, terrified, knowing they were close to death, asking themselves why and if their families would suffer the same fate. I felt chills, something horrible. When I was in the crematoriums, my skin got impregnated with the smell of death that the walls and floors still ooze. I could not continue with the tour and rushed back to the office."

"How hideous!"

"I think that when we are done here, I will never be the person I was before. It's not the same to read what happened during the Holocaust than to visit Auschwitz and see firsthand the place where this infamy took place. It's something that escapes human comprehension."

"Mariana, I feel guilty for having gotten you mixed up in this whole thing."

"No, Alex, I got involved in all this on my own accord and don't regret it."

"Don't worry, I will stay with you and will not leave till we have resolved this mystery. If I was that kid, why didn't my parents tell me?"

"You couldn't blame them. At the time, to be adopted was considered taboo and it was hidden from children and even relatives and friends. It's possible that they feared you wouldn't love them in the same fashion. Perhaps they wanted to protect you so that you didn't suffer on learning where you were born. I don't know."

"You know how much I loved them. I could've not have had better parents. Besides, I would've admired them even more, especially knowing that they had rescued me from a hell such as this one. It's obvious they gave me the opportunity of having a happy and normal life. What torments me the most is who then were my real parents? Are they still alive?"

"That worries me. You must be ready for whatever we might find. It may not be something pleasant."

The Auschwitz Center offices would be closed on the weekend, so that on Saturday they decided to explore Krakow. They visited the Wawel Castle, surrounded by lovely gardens with flowers in all colors and shapes. From the top of the hill they admired the Vistula River, which meandered gracefully in-between the city. They strolled around the Rynek Glowny, the largest square in Europe, crowded with people, where they enjoyed an open-air chamber music concert.

They walked around the Cloth Hall, a large building which was the center of commerce, now turned into a handicrafts market, where Mariana bought an embossed icon of the Black Madonna, the city's symbol. Alex gave her a two-colored Baltic amber bracelet. They finished their tour with a visit to the Wawel Cathedral, imposing with its spectacular interior of blue mosaics.

Afterwards they visited St. Mary's Basilica to see the fifteenth-century altar stolen by the Nazis in 1939, only recovered after the war in a Nuremberg castle. From the top of the church's taller towers, they saw how at the hour, a man dressed in sixteen-century fashion would give a trumpet signal, known as the *Heynal mariacki*, with an old-fashioned type of cornet, into the four cardinal points. They heard it several times while dining in front of the Basilica in one of the square's many cafés. Both tried Krakow's typical smoked cheese, the *oscypek*, and asked for a bottle of traditional Polish wine, *grzaniec galicyjski*.

In the square, before them, an ensemble played Mozart melodies.

"I am very grateful for what you are doing to help me," Alex told her.

"We are friends and, besides, it's a fascinating story."

"During the last couple of weeks, I have been thinking a lot and I feel very lonely."

"Your career has always been most important to you. You've gotten where you wanted. You are famous and the entire world applauds you. You can't complain: you've triumphed. It's what you wanted, right?"



"Correct, but I now realize my selfishness. I've decided that I am no longer going to make lengthy tours, only three or four concerts a year. A few conservatories have asked me to give occasional master classes to their most outstanding students. Also, the Berlin and Paris Symphony Orchestras have been after me for a while to accept their directorship. I will do something of the sort."

"Have you already told Pollot? All hell will break loose."

"I'll tell him as soon as this adoption mystery is resolved. Only then I'll be able to straighten out my thoughts, put my life in order and decide what to do with my career."

Mariana did not say a word, she only stared in silence.

Sunday was spent touring the streets of Kazimierz, the Jewish quarter, and they visited the small fifteenth century Remuh Synagogue. In the afternoon they went to a Dvořák concert performed by the Krakow Symphony Orchestra, in the Bonerowski Palace's Chopin Salon, close to the square. Later they dined not far from there, in a small restaurant, by candlelight. They shared some intimacies and remembered old times.

Early Monday morning they headed to Auschwitz. Mr. Rosenback received Alex and Mariana in his office.

"Welcome to the Center, Mr. York. The *Shoah*, the Holocaust, is not easy to understand. I am going to show you around Auschwitz I, Auschwitz II-Birkenau and Auschwitz III-Monowitz, which were the principal camps, although there were other additional ones by the same name. During our tour, please ask me all the questions you wish. I think it's essential for your investigation to learn what occurred at this place. That way you will better understand whatever findings you make."



When they reached the main gate, Mariana translated to Alex the meaning of the inscription that was visible over the iron main entrance gate: "*Arbeit macht frei,*" "Work will make you free." Alex fancied it a macabre, gruesome joke. He seemed to have gone speechless. He tried to imagine thousands of human beings terrorized as they crossed that gate, in route to a hellish final destiny where most of them would never return from.

Mr. Rosenback continued:

"Auschwitz was established in 1941 as a labor camp, but afterwards it was turned into an extermination center, where the Nazis insisted on carrying out the "Final Solution" to achieve a world free of Jews. Until Auschwitz's liberation, in January of 1945, six million human beings were murdered and abused, and not all were Jews."

"Weren't they all Jews?"

"There were gypsy prisoners, Jehovah Witnesses, Catholics, Evangelicals, homosexuals... Everyone that did not fit the Nazis' Arian profile they had pre-determined as the perfect man."

They saw the railroad tracks, the platform where the prisoners landed and the double barbed wire fence that surrounded the camp and which was electrified during the war.

Upon entering several gigantic barracks which were used as dormitories, some made of brick and others of wood, Alex tried to imagine how the life of those prisoners must have been in those conditions. "As you can see, the bunk beds were three stories high. In each, on miserable straw mattresses and without sheets, several individuals piled up. Often, the weight caused them to collapse and those underneath died crushed. Mortality rate was extremely high due to the diseases, malnutrition and the slave work that they were submitted to."



"What is that cement wall in the middle of the barracks, with holes in the center?" Alex inquired.

"Those were the latrines. The prisoners had to use them in front of all the other ones, without any privacy whatsoever and, due to the excessive amount of people in the barracks, the excrement overflowed. When they were unusable, the prisoners had to relieve themselves in corners, like animals. The stench was unbearable. Besides, very rarely could they bathe. Lice, fleas and diseases like typhus turned out to be endemic. The degradation to which they were subjugated was subhuman," Mr. Rosenback pointed out.

He then showed them the central yard where the roll calls took place. The gallows in the middle and the wall where the executions were carried out and which still exhibited a large dry bloodstain. "Death still hovers here," Alex thought.

They went inside the jail in block 11 and saw the ditches dug in the rock, where four naked prisoners were introduced, pressed against each other. In a slow death sentence, they would keep them standing for several days, without room to move, without water or food, without even taking them out to let them do their needs. When one died, the corpse would remain there with the others who were still alive. At first the screams and pleading could be heard, afterwards the wailing, the moaning. In the end, only silence remained.



Mr. Rosenback took them to block 10, a sort of laboratory of horrors.

"Here Dr. Mengele, the Medical Director of the Camp, worked. The prisoners referred to him as the 'Angel of Death' because anyone that fell underneath his claws rarely ended up alive. He and several other doctors carried out cruel experiments with the prisoners."

He explained how they would inflict wounds on prisoners, force them to withstand high temperatures, inoculate them with various viruses, or make them take poison to afterwards treat them or let them die, with the purpose of finding effective treatments to look after wounded German soldiers, or when these suffered from hyperthermia or fell sick. Sometimes, the doctors would amputate the affected limbs, at others they would allow for them to gangrene and to study the process.

"They also experimented with dwarfs or twins in search of a genetic code to create the perfect Arian man, in accordance with the Nazi model, and to find the formula to obtain multiple births. Like a paradox, science greatly advanced with those monstrosities because human beings were used as guinea pigs."

"What happened to those doctors after the war ended? I can't believe that their atrocities went unpunished," Alex asked.

“Although many of those so-called doctors escaped, some stood trial after the war and, as a result, a much stricter code of ethics was established for the medical profession,” he told them.

They approached block 24.

“Here, in 1943, the Nazis built a brothel to entertain the soldiers of the SS. At their beck and call, they chose the most attractive women prisoners. When an officer fancied any particular prisoner, he had her removed from the barracks and sent to the brothel. Some women committed suicide by throwing themselves against the electrified fences to avoid being used as sex slaves,” commented Mr. Rosenback.



They entered into the only gas chamber left standing in Auschwitz's original camp, which had recently been restored for the museum.

“I can imagine the peoples' terror when they were forced into this ghastly place and realized they were going to die,” Alex observed, while looking at the height of the grey, cold, dark and windowless enclosure, and noticing on the roof some small square apertures. Mariana also looked up. She was very pale. Alex noticed her frailty and held her arm, since she was about to faint.

“The soldiers ordered them to undress, making them believe they were going to take a shower. When they closed the entrance —noticing that something strange occurred since water was not coming out of the showers— the prisoners started banging the doors and screaming desperately. Meanwhile, another soldier was on the roof with a mask and introduced the gas Zyklon-B through the small openings that you can observe. The screams continued for several more minutes until they were no longer heard. The soldiers waited until everyone died and, afterwards, opened the doors to remove the corpses. Men, women and children were piled up, with the rictus of horror on their faces and stiff hands," the Director concluded, with a shaky voice.



They hastily left that place, with anguish reflected on their faces. What they had seen and the gruesome scene that that man had described to them, gave them the chills.

Lastly, they visited a nearby crematorium.

"Before 1942, the bodies were cremated outdoors. When Auschwitz was destined as the main center for extermination and thousands of people started arriving on a daily basis from all corners of Europe, they expanded the death machine, building Auschwitz-Birkenau as well as more gas chambers and crematoriums. There were forty-six ovens, each with room for in-between three and five people at a time. The incineration lasted on average half an hour, so that they could burn thousands of bodies daily. Moreover, we discovered dozens of enormous common graves with the remains of thousands of bodies and canalizations on the side to recover the bodies' fat. When there were too many bodies and the ovens didn't suffice, they incinerated them in the graves," Rosenback said.

Alex and Mariana were flabbergasted at the extent of such cruelty. And the Director concluded:

"The Nazis made use of everything: the fat extracted from the bodies was turned into soap. In the officers' cabins in Auschwitz, lamps and other artifacts made from the prisoners' skin were found. The belongings that were taken from them upon arrival were sent to a warehouse known as Kanada. Afterwards, the valuable items were classified and sent to a center in Berlin."

"Kanada?"

"Well, it was a euphemism. It should have been Canada, since it appears the Nazis held that country as a symbol of prosperity and wealth. That is why they named that large warehouse thus, where the prisoners' belongings were stored: clothing, shoes, reading glasses, gold teeth, jewelry, artwork, and even Jewish religious articles."



"What happened to the culprits of this death machine?" Mariana asked.

"Before the war was over, the high-ranking officers had already planned their escape and had secretly sent the stolen treasures to different countries. When the Nazis realized they were losing the war, they carried out their action plan. They used various avenues: diplomatic passports, protection from higher authorities as well as requesting political asylum. The "ratlines" were the most popular escape routes. Many tried to remain under the radar and changed their identities. Others did not even bother in hiding nor concealed their true name and were even listed in the city's telephone directory where they lived. For a long time, the world behaved with total indifference, even after the war had ended."

"I remember Eichmann's case, when the Mossad kidnapped him in Buenos Aires, where he lived peacefully, and took him to Israel to be tried," Alex remarked.

"Yes, it was a very high-profile case, an important victory for Simon Wiesenthal, who had been after him for years.

Nevertheless, even though he tried to grab Josef Mengele, he was unable to find him. This one lived out his last years peacefully in anonymity, until it is believed he drowned as an old man in a Brazilian beach," Rosenback replied.

"Many went unpunished, right?" Mariana asked.

"More than we would've wished. It was practically impossible to judge so many thousands of people, entire villages and even prestigious organizations that collaborated with the Nazis. Besides, it is said that ODESSA and another groups by the name of Spinne or Spider protected them through a complex web of disinformation and concealment, whose tentacles ran underground throughout the world. The Nazis used the money they stole from the Holocaust victims to buy their liberty and their lives."

"Were they able to catch those responsible for Auschwitz?" Alex asked.

"In the Frankfurt-Auschwitz trials, two of the cruelest women guards that were here were condemned to death: Maria Mandel and Irma Grese, the youngest Nazi to be tried. I think she was barely twenty-two. And Höess, the commander of Auschwitz, was also tried. He was hanged right here in 1947, before what were his living quarters."

"Fanaticism is frightening," Mariana remarked.

"Just to mention a well-known case… Goebbels and his wife remained by Hitler's side till the very end in this one's bunker in Berlin and, victims of his cult, decided to commit suicide and murder their six children, as proof of their loyalty to their Führer."

Very little remained unscathed in the Monowitz area, where the prisoners worked in infrahuman conditions for the great conglomerates and factories. Within the tall weeds, you could still see the chimneys and the remaining huge structures, now in ruins.

In silence, they headed back to the Archives' offices. Alex felt a terrible pain at the thought of perhaps being born in that place, in the middle of all the horror he had just listened to... wondering over and over what horrible story was there behind his birth. Alex was already sure he was the boy they were looking for. It was only a matter of time to confirm his suspicions. In the end, he only wanted to escape that godforsaken place.



"No one is capable of understanding the Nazis' atrocities, so it's normal that you feel the way you do," Nora told them when they were back at her the office, while serving them two cups of hot tea.

"Do you already know how many kids there were alive when the camp was liberated?" Alex asked Mariana.

"Till now I've only found twenty-eight. I was surprised that it was so few. Perhaps the Nazis didn't have time to kill them."

"Were they all male?"

"Thirteen were girls, so I didn't take into them into account. We are left with fifteen males, of which Nora has helped me identify eight. Six were adopted, but the names of the adopters do not coincide with that of your father. The other two died shortly thereafter and we were able to determine that they lived with their families."

"So, then there are seven non-identified males," Alex concluded.

"I presume that amongst them must be the one we are looking for."

Mariana excused herself and left the room to make a telephone call.

Nora, who overheard the conversation from her desk, came up to Alex and told him:



"On realizing that they were defeated, the Nazis forced the prisoners to set out on the "death march" to get them out of Auschwitz, but left the kids in the camp, mainly the smallest."

"How did they find them?"

"When the Russians liberated Auschwitz, they found practically a hundred kids, but only those twenty-eight Mariana spoke of earlier survived. The newly born were in a severe state of malnutrition and some had died. The oldest ones were found lost amongst the bodies that were strewn all over the camp."

"I am surprised they were able to document the identity of those children."

"In the middle of the reigning chaos, a great effort was made to record with as much accuracy as possible the survivors' information and especially that of children, to try and reunite them with their families. The United Nations created an agency –UNRRA- to coordinate this effort. Newspapers published lists and pictures, and the radio made announcements. In spite of it all, a lot of leads were lost, perhaps because time could not be invested to procure the children's well-being. Till this day we continue to trace the survivors, in case someone looks for them, as is the case with you now."

Mariana returned to the room, with happiness reflected on her face.

"Alex, good news… I have been trying for days to get a hold of a friend and colleague of mine at the University of Miami who was in the diplomatic service and with important connections in Washington, DC. I've just spoken to him from Mr. Rosenback's office. I sent him via fax the document and the power of attorney you gave me to take the necessary steps. He is going to try and get a copy of the legalization in the United States of the adoption papers. He says that most likely your mother also had to sign."



"I hope we can obtain something through that avenue."

***

That evening they dined in a small restaurant nearby the hotel, when Alex told her:

"Do you know what I did when I played Chopin's waltz in Paris?"

"No, tell me."

"I thought of you…"

Mariana smiled, but did not answer. Neither did she withdraw the hand Alex was caressing.

***

In the next couple of days, and with Nora's help, they identified three additional kids, but they ruled them out because they were not adopted either. Information on the four remaining children was confusing, but they were finally able to find out, after several telephone calls, that one was adopted by a Russian soldier and that, apparently, the mother had died. The other, some relatives took him in at the end of the war and went off to live in their village in the outskirts of Berlin.

The remaining two were twins and the information regarding them was not complete. All that was known was that they were born shortly before the Soviets' entrance and that the mother was confined to barrack 10 and was of German origin. But her name did not appear. One of the children was adopted by an American soldier. His name did not appear as well, since the adoption procedures took place in Münich. The whereabouts of the other was unknown.

"Twins?" Alex said with surprise.

"Nazis were fascinated by them. Sometimes they'd kill them, others they'd use for genetic experiments. The man in charge was the dreaded Dr. Josef Mengele or the 'Angel of Death,' as the prisoners would call him," Nora remarked.

Alex shuddered.

***

Days later, Nora handed Mariana a certified envelope that had just arrived addressed to her name from Washington, DC. She watched nervously from her desk.

Mariana held the envelope and looked at Alex, who also contemplated expectant. With shaking hands, she tore the paper, carefully took out its contents and read it in silence.

"Alex, here is the answer we were waiting for."

## Third movement – *Agitato tempestoso*

"Walk pigs, don't stop! Come on, faster, you're not on holiday!" the soldiers would yell, while we dragged our feet along the dusty path from the train station till the entrance to Auschwitz. Slow, as if that way we'd delay the arrival to our destination.

Some very high, never-ending electric barbed-wire fences surrounded the camp. In the gun turrets, with lit search lights, soldiers pointed at the newly arrived with their machine guns. The SS *Totenkopfverbände*, in charge of the camp's security, gave orders and the dogs surrounded us menacingly.

Vegetation was inexistent; there were no flowers or birds. Only the rough voice of the soldiers could be heard, which grew before nature's utter silence. A sticky smoke, a strange burnt smell floated in the air.

*In the midst of immense confusion, where everyone spoke and yelled at the same time, the megaphones announced repeatedly: "Women and children to the left, men to the right. Those who do not consider themselves fit to work for the Third Reich, must say so. They will be sent to do housework."*

*Prisoners were made to file by dozens of tables in which officials in white robes quickly determined their fate, barely looking at them. Old men, pregnant women, sick folk and small children were sent to the trucks stationed nearby, to be taken elsewhere.*

*Many of the newly arrived women wore a white scarf over their heads, in the fashion of the wives of the orthodox Jews. Mothers tried to keep their children under control so that they didn't move or cry, men protested, the young tried protecting their parents, the old did not understand why they were mistreated in such a manner. The guards cursed, yelled and separated them at their discretion. Chaos was total.*

*Vera held Rachael and Leah with cold sweaty hands. In a brief whisper, she warned them with firmness: "Don't separate from me for a single moment." Joseph looked at them from the men's line, with eyes blurry from impotence. They were not allowed to speak. In Leah's head, her father's warning boomed, turned into command: "We must be strong, we must survive."*

*Members of a unit known as the* Sonderkommando, *Jewish prisoners themselves, assisted the Nazis. They wore striped uniforms, just like the rest of the prisoners. Different from the rest, they walked with a hunch and with short, rhythmic steps. Of extreme leanness, these prisoners had a neutral expression on their faces; their eyes were sunken in their sockets surrounded by deep black bags.*

*In the line, in front of Vera, there was a young woman with a baby in her arms and an old woman by her side. One of the* Sonderkommando *men approached and gave her an order with a sense of urgency in his voice: "give the kid to the grandmother." The girl did not react. The man looked around him fearful, came close and repeated with firmness, but without raising his voice. This time the girl obeyed, without understanding why.*

*On reaching the tables, the grandmother and the baby were sent to the trucks. Desperate, the young woman threw herself at the feet of an SS officer, begging not to be separated from her family. The man kicked her with rage, pulled out his gun and shot her in the forehead. Blood spattered those who were nearby. Complete silence, no one reacted.*



The queue where father was standing moved quicker than ours and he was soon out of sight. I will never forget the sadness on his face, tight-lipped, his paleness, while he walked towards an uncertain destiny, knowing that he was leaving us behind, in hell. Mother, in a vain attempt of reassuring herself and us, told us that we would meet up with him again later somewhere in the camp, for upon arrival we had been told that the families would remain together.

One of the men garbed in a white robe asked us for our name and where we came from. Each of us was registered and received a number. We were then ushered into an enormous hall and ordered to undress. Ashamed to look at one another and to be before all those unknown people, the humiliation was lacerating. Rachel and I had never seen mother nude before. I closed my eyes; tears rolled down my cheeks. I felt mad, rage, a wish to scream, to flee, but where to?

Auxiliary women soldiers, known as the *aufseherinnen*, shaved our heads and all our body hair. It fell to the ground, at the same rhythm that our identity vanished. The same question kept resonating in my head: Why were we in Auschwitz? What was our crime?

Even more wounding was the laughter from the surrounding soldiers, their mean remarks, and the lust in their eyes. How could they make fun of us, defenseless women, naked and bald? Weren't they moved to compassion on seeing the elderly with flabby skin, and their faces furrowed by wrinkles? Didn't they have mothers, sisters, wives? Had women given birth to them or were they monsters conceived by evil?



Mother flushed with anger, Rachel very embarrassed. For the first time in my life, I was face-to-face with evil and could not help feeling an intense hatred burning within me. I wanted to die that very instant. God had abandoned us!

They allowed us to take a shower. The water was very cold, almost freezing, and we had no soap, but it was a relief to get rid of the filth somewhat. Mother and I had our legs splashed with blood, now dry, of the young girl murdered by our side. Once we finished showering, we were sprayed with some kind of green bleach, disinfecting and hot, that left a stinky mist on our skin.

After being left standing in the patio for several hours, naked and without towels to dry, they handed us some grayish uniforms, with blue and white stripes, made from some very crumpled coarse cloth. Each person was given a *winkel* or triangle, of a distinctive color, according to their ethnic group or classification the Nazis had decided. In the lower end of the triangle was the assigned number. We had to sew it on the left-hand side of our chest.

Rachel and I were given the brown color for being German, but there were others: green, pink, red or black. Mother's *winkel* displayed an F, which identified her as French. A young girl next to me had the letter Z, because she was a *zigeuner* or gipsy. We Jews also wore a yellow superimposed Star of David. Beneath the uniform we had no underclothes; we would use none again while in there.

We were struck to see, amongst the recently arrived prisoners, hundreds of Jehovah Witnesses or Bible students — *Bibelforschers*, like the Nazis called them— whose crime had been to refuse to make the Nazi salute and serve in the army. The SS confiscated their Bibles and made a pyre in the central patio, while they spit on them or laughed out loud. Weren't the soldiers so-called Christians? How come they made fun of their own sacred book?



I wondered where father could be and if he would be going through our same ordeal. We had never separated, and I could imagine his anguish not knowing about his family. The unknown crowded in my head, diatonic, unbearable.

Next to me an old woman dropped to the floor, we didn't know why. The SS pushed her several times with his foot and yelled at her to get up. She was dead. As she didn't move, he turned his back on her and continued giving out orders, as if what was on the ground didn't have the slightest importance. I tried deciphering if that woman had any relatives in that crowd, since no one approached her. We quickly dehumanized.

With shoves, we entered the *Haftlingsrankebau*, the hospital. The hall was immense and there were hundreds, perhaps thousands of women. Many screamed, others cried, others just walked disoriented from one place to another. Horrified, we saw that they would tattoo our left forearm with the number that had been assigned to us upon entering which, at first, we didn't know what it was for.

Several soldiers carried out the job with industrious efficiency, assisted by some prisoners of the *Sonderkommando,* which forcefully restrained us. Soldiers beat those that resisted. They used centimeter long needles, without sterilization or anesthesia: the same for all women. On finishing, they would rub our bleeding wounds with permanent ink. Blood gushed from the tattoo and the pain was unbearable, but we could not complain. They pointed their weapons at us and we no longer doubted they would shoot without hesitating.



Mother was tattooed with the number 71548. Rachel and mine followed in sequence. I wanted to tear my skin off then and there. How much we would end loathing that number which would follow us forever!

We had only been in Auschwitz for several hours and they had already turned us into mechanical beings, unexpressive, grotesque entities, sheathed in a ridiculous and crude uniform, hairless, will-less, nameless, and only identifiable by a tattooed number.

In an expression of pain and indignation, mother pressed her lips. Rachel's eyes were all puffed up from so much crying. I, in turn, was dazed and felt as if I'd been hit over the head. Hardly containing the rage and pain, my disgust and infinite hate toward those monsters was absolute. Where was God?

*Auschwitz I, the main camp, was immense, with rows of rectangular red brick barracks. Some were three; others four-stories high, all numbered. The majority were used as dormitories and the rest as offices, jails, infirmaries, hospitals and laboratories. The women's and men's sections were separated by a brick wall some two meters high. The* boklovas *or block chiefs, who competed in cruelty and sadism with the Nazi soldiers, supervised the women's dormitories.*

*Vera, Rachel and Leah were assigned to barrack number 12, with sixty wooden bunk-beds of three pallets each, covered by a thin layer of straw and paper sacks filled with shavings, in the manner of a mattress, without sheets or pillows. Each pallet could accommodate fifteen women. Since thousands of prisoners arrived daily from all corners of Europe, the crowding was unbearable. Often, the bunk-beds would collapse from the weight of the women and those on the bottom died crushed, so many preferred sleeping on the floor, between filth and insects.*

*When Vera and her daughters entered the barrack, they remained standing in the middle of the corridor, disconcerted, not knowing what to do. Hundreds of women screamed, pushing one another, trying to find a place where to settle. All the pallets seemed to be occupied.*

*"Come, there's space here," a soft voice called them, the first kind sound they'd heard in a long time. It was Ilse Babish, a young German Jewish woman from Berlin. She had dark eyes, big, expressive, and a sweet voice that radiated peace. She made room for Rachel and Leah in her pallet and found another one nearby for Vera.*

*Ilse was a young woman, kind and compassionate, who had been six months in Auschwitz. The Nazis had murdered her entire family. She worked in the infirmary and sometimes at the hospital. Risking her own life, she occasionally stole medicine to help the sick women prisoners in the barracks. They all respected her.*

*Latrines, always overflowing, were in the middle of the barrack. The stench was unbearable. There was no toilet paper. Showers were in another building and bathing was rare, depending on the guards' whims. There was no soap or towels. Prisoners smelt of urine, excrement, hunger. Fleas and lice thrived in the clothing, in the pallets… all over the place. The bites became wheals and then wounds that never healed. Typhus and diseases were a constant threat.*

At nine they ordered us to keep quiet and go to sleep. We felt painful stomach pangs and uncontrollable nausea. Mother, Rachel and I had been without food or water for practically two days. Wailing and moaning was heard in low voices. Horrified, we discovered that a rat colony and hundreds of roaches moved about the barrack and pallets. The woman who was by my side told me: "You'll have to get used to them, they're always here."

Mother tried to keep calm, impotency was reflected in her eyes and her hands shook. She spoke to us slowly and tried to cheer us, but even she didn't believe in what she told us. Rachel cried out of control. I couldn't cry; didn't want to show weakness. Forcing myself to be strong, deep down I was nothing but a frightened child, as much or more than the others.

The smoke and strange stench we'd felt upon arrival invaded the barrack, and the nausea it produced was unbearable. All the searchlights remained beaming all night long and their brightness inundated the barrack's interior. I thought I'd lost my soul that first night in Auschwitz, but decided to promise myself to remain undefeated, to fight to survive, to honor my promise to father. Hugging my mother and sister in search of safety that they couldn't give me either, exhaustion totally overpowered me. I don't know how I fell asleep.

One early morning, at four, we heard a deafening reveille and the screams of the *boklovas* for us to wake up and go to the *zaehlappel* or roll call, which meant standing for hours, formed in rows of ten in the Appelplatz, the central patio, no matter what the weather was like outside. These took place in the early morning before we set out for work and again in the afternoon upon our return. On Saturdays, to transgress our *Shabbath*, they kept us standing and forbidden to move, for hours on end.



The first day at the camp, an SS asked those who did not consider themselves apt for work or to stand roll call to speak up. An old lady, recently arrived, raised her hand, while the rest tried to stop her.

"It's true, I am 77 and have no strength to work," she said with determination.

"*Komm*," the soldier answered her with kindness.

She came close, he made a gesture and another soldier shot her.

"...Like a macabre trick. Cold, hungry, because she is elderly and sick, the woman confesses to her weakness and becomes an accessory to the brutal act. That is how they justify the punishment and, in the end, oneself is responsible for one's own death," I thought horrified.

Immediately, we heard through the loudspeakers that the guards would kill anyone who fainted or refused to work. Every day we would see the threat carried out. The body could remain in the same place for hours, sometimes still in the throes of agony, till we saw it expire. No one could come close to it or succor it.



Food was always the same and very often in a state of decay. In the morning, half a cup of dirty water which they called coffee or tea, without sugar, but which at least warmed us up a little, especially during the merciless winter. Lunch consisted of a bowl of soup with some vegetables, sometimes raw, and once a week a smelly piece of sausage or two spoonfuls of some clots of milk which was meant to be cheese.

At night they would serve us a diluted and insipid broth, with potato peels or turnips, accompanied with a small piece of stale bread in which flour was mixed with sawdust. On some occasions they would serve us a spoonful of marmalade. Very often we would hide the piece of bread to eat at some other moment, when the stomach pangs became unbearable.

We would usually find cockroaches and other insects in our food, but we would just discard them. If we wanted to survive, we had to eat something. Hunger was our constant companion. Rations were meager and the lines very long. Many times, that attempt of food was not enough for everyone and the last would end up with an empty plate. Sometimes the soldiers would purposely trip the prisoners, so that their food would fall on the ground. In an animal instinct of preservation, they would desperately fall on their knees and, with trembling hands, try to pick up whatever they could. Soldiers would mock their feat and forced them to lick the floor.

Work squadron supervisors were the *kapos* —German criminal delinquents for the most part— who collaborated with the Nazis. They wore an armband over the striped uniform and received petty privileges for their services, like a little more food or a mat to sleep. The rest of the prisoners despised them. Truthfully, I don't think they had any other option: they couldn't refuse. In the end, the Nazis always killed them.



Mother was assigned to the Kanada warehouse, where the confiscated belongings of the newly arrived were sent. Her job consisted in classifying and wrapping the objects. She would tell us that there were religious artifacts there, documents, fine clothing, baby carriages, musical instruments, and much more. She tried surreptitiously to locate my violin, but never saw it.

Hundreds of people carried out different tasks. A brigade —closely watched over by armed soldiers— unstitched the lining of coats and unglued the soles of shoes taken from the prisoners in search of valuable items that might be hidden there. They'd frequently find diamonds, gold, jewelry and money.

Other women, under the supervision of several guards, kept a detailed record of the articles, which would afterwards be wrapped by category and sent in special trains to a destination unknown to the prisoners, but which were believed to be some warehouses at the Nazi general headquarters in Berlin.

We would walk for three hours every day to Monowitz, Camp III of the factories, also known as Buna. It was an immense area with dozens of long barracks and very wide chimneys, where we worked for ten or eleven hours and thus get the most out of daylight, under the surveillance of the dreaded *kapos*. The only time for a break was the half hour lunch. If anyone broke the rules or didn't do their tasks with the efficiency and quickness expected, she was killed on the spot. In the afternoon the trucks would come by to pick up those that had died that day.



Rachel was assigned to the IG Farben, one of Germany's most prestigious companies, which used slave labor to produce its liquid fuels and synthetic rubber. The chemicals caused skin eruptions in Rachel and other women that would never heal because they lacked the appropriate medicines.

My job was at the quarry, where we had to carry blocks of stone, shapeless and irregular, with cutting edges, which required at least two persons to transport. The terrain was steep, and when it rained became swampy. Resembling clogs, the wooden shoes we wore frequently slipped from our feet and caused blisters. We would frequently stumble and loose our balance, the stones falling and injuring us. Meanwhile, the *kapos* and the guards ordered us with screams and shoves to walk quicker. If we didn't get up right away, they would strike us or even shoot us.

On seeing my bloody hands, full of wounds and blisters, I was frightened to death to lose the mobility in my fingers. The only thing that kept me going in that inferno was my desire to become a solo violinist someday: my *leitmotiv*. Even though it was distant, I resisted giving up my dream. That gave me the strength to keep going on.

We would return to the main camp by foot on finishing the day's work in Monowitz. There we would be searched in case we'd hidden a morsel of bread, a potato, anything that was prohibited to us. If they found anything, the consequences could be severe and could even spell death.

Punishment was meted out in the main patio, with the prisoner naked before the other prisoners and soldiers. It could depend on the soldier's frame of mind: she might be tied to a rack and beaten with a club or a whip while being forced to count out loud the number of blows "one, two, three…" or was ordered to stand still naked before the reflectors the entire night, with her hands to her nape. If the prisoner fainted before sunrise, the soldier in the turret would shoot her. The German shepherds were trained to kill. At the order of "Jews," the soldiers would let loose the dogs' clasp and these would attack the prisoners that were before them.

As soon as we arrived, the prisoners that had been there longer told us that the Nazis gassed the people they took in the trucks and would then burn the bodies. At first we found it hard to believe, but the rarefied air was undeniable: the nauseating smell and that thick smoke that constantly produced the grey drizzle of dust were clear-cut proofs. We soon realized that what stuck to our skin was the residue of human beings, most likely from our relatives. An intense smell of hell floated among us: the presence of death was inescapable and omnipresent in Auschwitz.

Mother was distressed. She would repeat to us not to disobey or defy the soldiers, to try and pass unnoticed. "This place is hell and those Nazis are the devils," she would tell us. She suffered a lot on our behalf, and for not knowing anything about father. Progressively skinnier and weaker, she was wasting away by the day.

Horrified, we witnessed the selections they made to eliminate those who no longer served for slave work or with the purpose of making space in the barracks for the newly arrived. They would order us to undress and congregate us in the main patio: a very efficient method of stripping us from our last shred of dignity and decency.

Nazis would start with the "Muslims," pseudonym given to the dirty and smelly prisoners whom the beatings, the inanition and the emptiness from the murder of their loved ones had transformed into the living dead. Of extreme leanness, "Muslims" exhibited protruding cheekbones and sunken unexpressive eyes, with yellowish parchment-like skin, full of sores and glued to the bone, and thread-like hair. With hardly audible voices, shaking uncontrollably and moving ever so slowly, they came across like zombies. Hallucinations from hunger, only reacting to what was in front of them when screamed at, resulted in total indifference from their end. Not one protested when beaten and only died when they could no longer resist.

Next, it was turn for the elderly and the weakest. A skin rash, any indication of frailty or inability to work meant a death sentence. The soldiers would be in the habit of going to the infirmary and hospital to remove the sick and drag them to the gas chamber. Sometimes, we'd prick our fingers to draw blood and then rub it on our cheeks, to look healthy and not be taken away.

We would learn, in time, that in Auschwitz not everyone was Jewish. There were also Christians, whose crime had been to protect Jews or had been wrongly accused. It was common to see nuns, priests, evangelical ministers as well as Jehovah Witnesses arrive in the trains; gypsies, also called *roma*, because they were nomads and different; disabled people because of their "imperfection" according to the Arian prototype that the Nazis had adopted at their will; homosexuals whom they intended to "rehabilitate."

More trains loaded with prisoners arrived from the four corners of Europe every day. They kept us abreast of the latest events, of the Nazis' advance and, especially, of the proliferation of concentration camps in Poland, Germany, Holland and Czechoslovakia. Auschwitz seemed to be the worst one, a large-scale machinery of death, where sooner or later we were all destined to die. We didn't know how: perhaps a bullet shot, in the gas chamber, torn to pieces by the guards' dogs, from beatings, of inanition or from some illness. Death was a reality. There was no way to escape it.



At three kilometers from the main camp, we were certain that the Nazis were building something on a large scale because we could see the constant movement of many prisoners on their way to work as well as lots of children, some very young, whose life had been spared to be employed as slaves.

Soon thereafter, Auschwitz II-Birkenau was inaugurated, and it was announced through the loudspeakers that a great number of female prisoners would be transferred. The guards would enter the barracks and force the women out with pushes and shoves. We immediately realized that they were planning an extraordinary selection to get rid of the human surplus and not have to take it to the new camp.

Quickly, we hid underneath some pallets. Rachel fell behind so I quickly grabbed her and dragged her to where mother was, barely a moment before two SS entered. They came so close to our hideout that we could see their boots a few feet away and could feel their impatient footsteps. We held our breath, with our heads glued to the ground. A rat came very close to us. My sister was terrified and shaking. Mother covered her mouth in case a sound escaped from her, while my sister looked at her imploringly with wild eyes. The men soon left, the stench in that place was unbearable and we knew they were afraid of contracting typhus. Most of the women in our barrack were taken to the gas chamber. Very few of us were transferred to Birkenau. That day we outwitted death.



The new barracks were wooden and, at least at first, clean. Since every day the trains brought hundreds —thousands of people— soon the space was insufficient. And as we were scarcely allowed to bathe or had running water to wash our uniforms, it wasn't long before the filth and lice returned.

Perplexed and with absolute horror we realized that, at the farthest ends of Birkenau, the Nazis had built several crematoriums with underground entrances. Some enormous chimneys stood, nothing resembling the ones at the main camp. It was obvious that the extermination process would be even more efficient now. Eventually, it would prove to be easier than having to incinerate thousands of bodies in the open air, stacked in mass graves, as they had done till then.

A motorcade of black cars arrived for the inauguration, large and elegant, with little red flags carrying the black swastika on the front. The most famous Nazi chiefs and political leaders came together, with their full-black uniforms, accompanied by hundreds of elite soldiers, for a grand celebration. Some even commented that Hitler would attend. They congregated before the main building, which stood out because of its tower and immense archway. Beneath it was where the trains entered daily, full of new prisoners. The major celebration was the installation of the new gas chambers and several crematoriums. To prove the new system's effectiveness, thousands of prisoners were sent to the gas chambers that day. The Nazi hierarchy was delighted beyond belief.



Two days later, one afternoon, Ilse arrived all shuddering, pale and about to faint. She had witnessed how the soldiers brought the children that had worked in the construction of Birkenau to the hospital, and how they'd been murdered, one by one, with phenol injections to their hearts. They inaugurated the crematoriums with them. From that moment on, at any hour, the chimneys spewed black smoke. The stench of burnt fat and flesh became unbearable. We lived with constant nausea.

In the following months, the Nazis would enlarge Birkenau several times to make room for more prisoners. Moreover, they built other crematoriums in Auschwitz I, the main camp. The death machine became ever more systematic. They were determined to exterminate us, totally.

The Nazis inaugurated in Birkenau a section to classify and wrap the murdered prisoners' prosthesis and gold teeth; the prisoners' hair, which would be used as raw material for tapestry; the ashes that came from the crematoriums that would become plant fertilizer. Everything was sent to warehouses in Berlin in the trains that would have otherwise returned empty. Women that had to work in that section would often have nervous breakdowns and many would commit suicide. How many of them must have wondered if those ashes or that hair, or those teeth or prosthesis would be their parents, their brothers, their sons, their husbands! I kept working at the quarry, almost preferring that task. Being assigned to work in a warehouse would have been unbearable for me.

Right at the start of winter, the temperature plunged several degrees below zero. It was torture to be in the open air during the daytime and at night we could hardly withstand the strong cold wind that penetrated through the cracks in the wood. Our hands and feet would freeze. We had no coats, even though there were thousands in the Kanada warehouse, according to what mother and other women who worked there had told us. The blankets they gave to us had a foul smell and were so raggedy that they barely protected us from fierce cold.

When the snow melted, it mixed with the dirt and became a sticky sludge. Many of us had wooden shoes, with no socks. The grazing of the skin produced very painful sores. We would often slip and fall to the ground. Mother tore up part of our shabby bedspread and made strips so that Rachel and I could wrap our feet.

Obsessed with not losing the notion of time —to decipher in what day, in what month and in what year we lived in— we prisoners would repeat every day to each other: "What day is it today? Are you sure?" Some would go to a lot of trouble to keep count, but none were sure to have it right. We needed to know how long we'd been there, although we didn't know till when or for what. Every day was like the previous, or worse.

At night, when the lights went off, several women would intone prayers, sometimes the *Shemoneh Esrei* of the sixteen benedictions, others the *Shema Yisrael*, or the *Avinu Malkeinu*. On Friday evenings, we would recite the *Kiddush* to wait for the *Shabbath*. Of course, without the wine or the silver cup; only a few pieces of stale bread that we keep for the occasion, evading the guards. We would also take on the task of retelling stories of the Jewish people. In those circumstances, it was the only way in which we could preserve our beliefs and our history. We could not allow for them to annihilate us in that fashion.

Living in constant fear, prisoners often would go mad or commit suicide. Everything was forbidden, with or without reason; anyone could be sent to the gas chamber. Going to death without knowing why... What had we done to deserve this?



One night, in the barrack, we noticed a young woman in a strange attitude. The sister had just died and was lying by her side. She looked at the body with a strange expression, incapable of reacting, of crying or uttering a word. We spoke to her, but she did not answer, as if she had turned into stone. For the entire night, she remained in the same position next to the corpse, rocking to and fro with a frightening rhythm. At dawn, walking like an automaton to the central patio for the morning roll call and displaying the same neutral expression on her face, she didn't stop in the queue as usual. The guard ordered her to halt and she ignored him. Immediately, she was shot in the back. I always thought it was a suicide.

I was convinced that our only way out was death, the sooner the better. Several times I considered the idea of throwing myself against the electric fences, as I had seen other prisoners do, but my cowardice or perhaps a primal sense of survival incomprehensible at the time was stronger than reason. Father's words hammered away in my head and prevented me from doing so. Besides, mother did not deserve that.

We did not know if father was still alive or not. The uncertainty was heartrending. I tried to be strong, to keep my sanity, but powerlessly witnessed my own collapse and that of our family. Rachel was always crying and depressed. Mother, now speechless, was becoming paler by the day with her eyes fading, blurry from sadness, until the symptoms of the dreaded typhus were patent.



"Leah, today they brought a prisoner to the infirmary who says he is a doctor. I think it's your father, for I believe I heard him say that his surname was Felton," Ilse told me one night, in a whisper.

"It's him! He is alive! How is he?"

"He's very thin, emaciated and weak like everyone else."

"Did he tell you anything?" I anxiously asked.

"Prisoners are not allowed to talk to one another. I can try if we are left alone for a while, but that's not very frequent."

"We must tell mother and Rachel."

"Your sister is not strong like you, precisely the reason I decided to talk first to you. You know her, and it must be you who tells her. And your mother, I will not lie to you Leah, I think she has typhus. She doesn't look well at all and I am not sure how much longer she can hold out. If they allow us to take her to the infirmary perhaps she can recover somewhat, but we hardly have any medicine. On the other hand, I am afraid that your father will not be able to hold back the emotion of seeing her. If the Nazis realize it, they're capable of killing them both."

"Try talking to him, to warn him. Please, tell him we are alive, that we love him very much and that I have not forgotten what he asked of me. That he too must be strong. We must leave this place alive to once again be a family. Tell him we think of him often, that we love him," I said to her. Without being able to hold back my feelings, I cried. My father was alive!

I repeated over and over: "father is alive and works in the infirmary," till convincing myself that they would not kill him as long as he was useful to them. Unable to sleep that night, I told my sister about my conversation with Ilse.



"All the wealth in the world means nothing… If only I could just see him again, even for an instant! How much do I miss father! And mother is dying, Leah." She told me tearfully.

Unable to find words to answer her, and feeling totally impotent, I could only hug her. My sister had changed drastically. It was painful for me to witness her suffering and how, forcefully and in a short time, she had transformed herself into a grown woman, but very fragile. She did not look pretty anymore; I no longer envied her. How much I would have given to go back in time!

Mother was very feeble now. For days, Rachel and I would lie on the floor with her, in a corner, because the rest of the prisoners did not want her to come near them for fear of getting infected. No one could survive typhus there, but my sister and I didn't care. One night, mother began shaking non-stop, with a very high fever. She could hardly recognize us. I was terrified that she could no longer go to work. They would notice her absence at roll calls and go fetch her at the barrack to kill her, as they had done so many times before with other prisoners.

At dawn she became delirious, completely unconscious. I looked at her ashen face, open-mouthed, wheezing. She was so skinny, so emaciated! Deeply moved by remembering her past beauty, her eyes full of life, her mane now absent, and her laughter, I tried recalling the happy moments: when she sat in our home's drawing room, the delicious smell of her baked bread which woke us in the morning, the way in which she received father in the afternoon when he'd return from his practice, her caresses, even her reprimands… Our family had disintegrated.



Before she had entered the hell she would never come out of, I engraved mother's image the way I wanted to remember her: carefree and happy. Nothing would ever again be the same. Rachel and I cried inconsolably. We hugged, kissed and told her how much we loved her. We wanted to believe that her soul understood us.

It was imperative to take mother to the infirmary for a doctor to see her, regardless of the danger this would entail if the soldiers came to fetch the sick to take them to the gas chamber, as they often did. In any case, she was in danger of death and it was the only possibility of helping her. Ilse called the *boklova* on duty whose name was Anika —a surly and disagreeable woman who walked like an elephant tumbling along— to ask her permission to take mother to the infirmary. At first she refused, but consented when Ilse told her it might be typhus. Rachel and I tried to accompany her, but the *boklova* gave us a push and screamed at us emphatically to stay.

Like a rag doll, mother looked incoherent and helpless. Ilse, our dear friend dragged her away, oblivious to the fact that she herself could contract the disease. Heartbroken, we could see her disappear, with the knowledge that we wouldn't see her again. That night, my sister asked me devastated: "Why

Leah, why?" I had no answer. Since our arrival at Auschwitz, I had asked myself that same question over and over.

That day we worked on tenterhooks, like automatons. The uncertainty was harrowing. We guessed the answer Ilse would bring in the afternoon. Defeated —in a state of bleak and dismal emptiness— almost not daring to look at us in the eye, she told us:



"There were several Nazi doctors when we arrived at the infirmary. Felton was also there. With a gloomy face, he helped me put Vera on a cot. I was afraid of his reaction, but he managed to contain himself. Only I noticed his sorrow, his sadness. She opened her eyes and looked at him in the light's glare. She tried saying something and expired calmly. Felton only tilted his head and turned around, so his tears would not betray him."

We cried in silence. Ilse was at a loss for words to console us. Mother had broken free from hell, she told us. She would no longer suffer; they would no longer hurt her. That we knew, but we would miss her a great deal. We loved her so much! Mother had died, and father perhaps we would never see again. My sister and I had been left alone. "Neither will she see his daughters die," I thought to myself. I felt an indescribable relief, for which I have always felt guilty.

That night we intoned in a low voice and with tears in our eyes the *Kaddish*, our mourning prayer, that which the children pronounce for their parents when these die, the *Orphan's Kaddish*: "*Yitgadal veyitkadash shme raba,*" (May His great name be exalted and sanctified.) This is how it begins and is repeated. Other prisoners joined in to complete the *Minyan*, the required quorum.

Ilse hugged us for a long while. That young woman had become our sole family, the only affection we had in that infernal place. I realized at that moment she could understand the magnitude of our pain because she too had lost her entire family. The three of us would be sisters from now on.



A few days later, Ilse managed to outwit the guards and speak to father. He was very sad and worried for Rachel and me, but she assured him we were fine and that she would look after us until we could join him. Father sent word that he loved us, to resist, that we would soon be together. If he had only seen the conditions we were in! Weeks later he did not return to work in the infirmary. Ilse learnt that he had been transferred to another camp. We never had news of him again.

*Rachel and Leah had been in Auschwitz for almost a year when, on a sunny May afternoon, they made the prisoners stand to attention in the patio to welcome in style a new personality: the* Lagerarzt, *the medical director.*

*Joseph Mengele had arrived.*

*A large parade was organized in his honor, while the soldiers sang the* Horst-Wessel-Lied. *In the morning, prisoners were allowed to bathe, for which some smelly and sticky soap bars were handed out which hardly lathered. In spite of this, it was inevitable that the prisoners' emaciated and humiliated appearance contrasted that of Mengele, who wore an impeccable officer's SS uniform, high boots, a gilded cockade on the lapel and a cross around the neck. On his cap, he had the death's-head badge and on his belt, the motto "With God's Blessing." The shiny buckle glared in the sun's rays.*

*His attraction and elegance emanated a subtle charm, almost an aura of perfection, which impressed certain women. Nevertheless, his aspect was far from the Arian figure that the Nazis had chosen as the prototype of the perfect man: skinny, average height, dark chestnut hair and small greenish eyes that came close together at the bridge of a prominent nose. He had quite a noticeable space in-between his upper front teeth.*

*Prisoners were clueless as to who had just arrived, but it was clear that it was someone important. They would find out soon enough.*

*Sometime afterwards, Mengele introduced himself during roll call and asked who played a musical instrument. Rachel and Leah raised their hand. There was already a male orchestra in the camp and a women's orchestra was in gestation: the* Madchenorchester von Auschwitz. *Playing in the orchestra meant a higher probability for the women prisoners to stay alive, better treatment, more frequent baths, shedding the crude striped uniform, eating a little better and staying away from hard work.*

*The prisoner Alma Rosé had just arrived, Gustav Mahler's niece, a famous Austrian violinist arrested in Holland and who had directed the* Wiener Waltzermadeln – *the Vienna Waltzing Girls Orchestra. Mengele immediately recognized her and ordered her to have his idea made reality because, in his own words, "the Germans loved good music and wished to enjoy it while working." The orchestra would be under the supervision of the* SS Oberaufseherin *Maria Mandel, the chief guard, who became the orchestra's benefactress and protector.*

*Maria Mandel, an Austrian a little over thirty, had just been transferred from the Ravensbruck Camp as a reward for her great working capacity, which had caught her superiors' attention.*

*Despite her prominent jaw, bushy eyebrows and a thick and heavy body, one could not say she was ugly. Her efficiency knew no limits and neither did her cruelty, especially towards women and children. The prisoners called her* "The Beast."



We followed Alma to the barrack destined for the orchestra. Its members would practice and live there. Arranged on some tables were some tables with an assortment of instruments which had been confiscated from the prisoners, some useless: several violins, violas, flutes, two cellos, an oboe, an accordion, and a piccolo. I wondered who their previous owners and their fate had been. Surely, if they were still alive, they would miss their instruments the same way I missed my Guarneri. Each one had to choose one she liked or her own, if she could locate it. My Guarneri, with its unmistakable blue case, was not there. I had to conform myself with a violin of a rather opaque sonority.

Alma was Jewish, but had converted to Christianity. She must have been in her forties, medium height, with vivacious brown eyes and a firm stride. I met her with her head shaved, but later realized that her hair was light chestnut brown and curly. She behaved as if she had been hired to direct the orchestra of a distinguished concert hall. We were struck by her pride and self-confidence. Alma commanded respect from the Nazis and even seemed not to be afraid of them. Despite her Jewish origin and now a prisoner, it was plain that Mengele and Mandel felt admiration and respect towards her.

Each one of us played before Alma in something resembling an audition, which Mandel also had to approve. It had been a long time since I had last played and my hands showed much damage from the work in the quarry. Afraid of not being able to produce one single harmonic sound and about to give up the opportunity, nervously, I decided to stay. Besides, there was nothing to lose.

Choosing to perform the *Chaconne* from the Second Partita for Solo Violin by Bach, I tuned the violin the best I could, even though my hands were shaking upon bringing the instrument to my shoulder. At first, my fingers were stiff but, gradually, they once again discovered the strings. Closing my eyes, I imagined being free, elsewhere, aspiring to play in a prestigious orchestra. The notes began to flow, inundating my senses and the music made my deepest wounds disappear, at least for a while.



"Enough, that shall do, you play very well. Your technique is impeccable; one can tell you vibrate to the music's time. I congratulate you; you have all the makings of a soloist."

Amazed at Alma's words, I suddenly opened my eyes. Even in the undeniable reality in which I was in, that eulogy coming from an excellent violinist like her moved me. It was reassuring to confirm that my dream was still alive, that the Nazis had not been able to shatter it. At that moment, feeling invincible and with renewed strength to persevere, I told myself: "Nothing in the world will defeat me. Father was right, I'm strong."

The candidates' level was uneven. Although some turned out to be good performers, the majority was mediocre. Alma did not reject those who were no good. She named me as first violin and at the cello a young woman by the name of Anna, daughter of a very famous Polish cellist. Around forty women made up the original orchestra, composed of several violins, violas, two violoncellos, an accordion, two mandolins, and three flutes.

Categorically and without beating around the bush, the first thing she told us was that if we wanted to be part of the orchestra, we would have to obey her and practice a great deal. Some considered her a despot and even a Nazi sympathizer, but deep down that was her way of saving us from death. We all understood we would play to gain time —one day at a time— and to stretch what we had left of life. How well I remembered mother's words when she told us repeatedly to study, that music would always come in handy in life!



Alma requested to have a piano brought from the Kanada warehouse for Rachel, but it wasn't possible. Mandel decided that Rachel could not stay in the orchestra and returned her to the common barracks. Alma reasoned that she could put her in charge of the musical scores and of some orchestration, but it was denied to her.

I wanted to go back with my sister, but Alma did not allow me to. Being a very good violinist and therefore needed in the orchestra, Mandel ordered me to stay. Alma, in an aside, told me that she would again try to get a piano; that she would not give up in her effort to rescue Rachel. Devastated, I felt alone and forlorn. What else were these monsters going to strip me of? My only consolation was that my sister returned to the same barrack where Ilse was.

An immediate disinfection process to rid us of lice and fleas followed at the hospital. Afterwards —transferred to a barrack destined for the orchestra— we showered. Our new uniforms consisted of a white blouse and a dark blue skirt, allowing us to finally shed the odious and coarse striped uniform. From now on we'd be able to bathe more often and wash our clothes. There was no overcrowding in our new room, the bunks were better and we even enjoyed the comfort of a mattress and a blanket, even if thin. Neither were there rats or other insects. Though not very big, rehearsals would take place in an additional lounge. I missed my sister and felt guilty of being able to enjoy those small perks that, in those circumstances, were almost a luxury.



Being a masterful performer, Alma perfectly knew the instruments' tessitura, their technical limitations, and how to obtain the best mixture of pitches. Without a doubt, she was a virtuoso. I volunteered to help her out in the orchestrations and, in the process, she taught me a great deal.

A few days later, a prisoner discreetly handed me the first of various messages from Ilse, giving me news of Rachel. It didn't surprise me because I knew she had access to some medicines, which served to buy off the *kapos* and other prisoners. This was the way she could help other prisoners send messages to their relatives. She risked her life, and so did I. Hence, I was able to receive frequent news of my sister.

Mandel procured an extensive selection of scores from the Kanada, amongst the confiscated belongings of the prisoners. We put together our repertoire with works such as *The Merry Widow*, Offenbach's "*Barcarolle*," waltzes by Strauss, German songs, and military as well as other types of marches. Of course, music by Jewish composers was forbidden. The Nazis called it *entartete musik*, degenerate music. We had to be very careful: our upcoming debut performance had to be absolutely flawless.

To launch the women's orchestra, Maria Mandel ordered us to get ready to offer a concert to the officers in the new

Birkenau Camp. Mengele was enthusiastic and sat in the first row. Alma played the *Czárdás* by Monti. I played Paganini's Caprice No. 16 and a transcription of the aria "Un bel di vedremo" from *Madame Butterfly* by request from Mandel, as it was her favorite opera.



Anna electrified everyone with her rendition of the First Suite for Solo Cello by J. S. Bach. Afterwards, she played a selection from the third movement of the Cello Concerto in B Minor by Dvořák. As it was martial, the soldiers loved it, especially Mengele. Moreover, we offered an assortment of German songs and other popular pieces. The Nazis sang along and applauded enthusiastically. Alma looked at us satisfied. The orchestra's quality was established and our lives were safe, at least for now.

Mengele ordered Alma for us to perform a concert every Sunday afternoon; to take advantage of the fact that it was not a working day. We always began our concerts with Wagner's *Overture of the Mastersingers of Nuremberg.* For the orchestra members, this meant an additional load of rehearsal time that left us without a day's rest, but to please the Nazis and for them to be satisfied with the music was better than marching toward the gas chamber.

The first Sunday concert was dedicated to Maria Mandel for her recent promotion to *Schutzhaftlagerführerin.* From then on, she would be the highest-ranking chief, in charge of all the *boklovas* and of the women's barracks. In addition to the new post, Mengele wanted her to remain as the orchestra's benefactress. She loved that; it made her feel important.

*Soon thereafter Irma Grese arrived in Auschwitz, the new* Oberaufseherin, *a position held till then by Maria Mandel. She, hardly twenty years old, surpassed Maria in cruelty and sadism. Although short, with a thick rounded body, she had a lovely face, framed by a mane of long blond hair which shone in the sun, making her stand out. Her large eyes were cold, penetrating, which contrasted with her sensual mouth. She always carried a whip in her hand and didn't hesitate to use it at will. She referred to Jews as "insects."*



*It was commented at the camp that Grese was Mengele's lover because they were often seen walking together, but others refuted that by saying she was a lesbian. The truth is that Grese would inflict sexual punishment on the prisoners, some very elaborate and of an inconceivable sadism. If a prisoner was particularly beautiful, the more ruthless became her torture. She sometimes selected several women, forcing them to work for her in the nude. The chores included serving food, scrubbing floors or any other task Grese would fancy. Prisoners soon realized that she was worse than Mandel. They called her* "The Hyena."

Anna and I were practically the same age and we both loved music. We practiced and performed as soloists. I felt very lonely, because Ilse and my sister were not close anymore. So, it was wonderful to have a friend to talk to who shared the same musical interests. Even though Anna was Polish, we could communicate without any difficulty whatsoever because she spoke French and German. She cried very often because, since arriving in Auschwitz, she knew nothing of her mother or sister. Their father had died before being transferred to the camp. I lacked the words; didn't know what to say as I too needed comforting. Hence, any other effort on my behalf to cheer her up would have been useless.



Alma demanded the utmost, highest and absolute quality from us as well as the best sound possible: a goal very hard to achieve in such a disparate group in terms of talent, brought together by destiny in a place where terror reigned and where there was no room for music. She always asked for more: "That *rubato* can improve," "that's not the correct *tempo*," "improve your *pizzicati*," "it's not quite right, let's do it again," "the *vibrato* and the *tremolo* are not defined," "it still doesn't sound right," "come on, more power," "again, let's take it from the top." Alma was tireless, relentless, and constantly expected more and more from us all. Naturally, the orchestra's level improved daily.

Seeing Alma worn out from work at nighttime, I think she took on that vertiginous rhythm to be dazed —submerged in music— and to not realize what was happening around her. Perhaps it was her way of escaping reality, to tame her own ghosts.

We'd play in the main entrance under the open sky, for hours on end, during the daytime, at night, cold, warm, or raining. By then, executions took place before all the prisoners, so the orchestra was placed in front of the execution wall between blocks 10 and 11, right near the central patio. The back-end wall was painted in black, with sand in front to absorb the blood of the dead. On dragging the bodies to the crematorium, the trail of blood tainted the streets of Auschwitz.

In the middle of the square, where the daily roll call took place, were the gallows, the preferred punishment inflicted to those who attempted to break out or dared to confront the soldiers. The sentence was read out loud, first in German and then in Polish. A prisoner chosen at random had to be the executioner. The condemned would climb on top of a box, the noose tied around his neck, a lever was pulled, the boxed kicked and the body would fall loose. Death was not immediate. The SS and the rest of prisoners watched expressionless while the hanged man writhed in agony from asphyxia and then expired.

Prisoners were forced to march at the beat of the music and to witness the executions, motionless for hours, without flinching, even if the executed were family or a friend. The orchestra had to perform until commanded to stop. Under those circumstances, the thought of coming across father or sister at any moment terrified me. My most fervent wish was that perhaps, in those last dying moments, we diminished their pain on their way to that absurd, atrocious and macabre death. The orchestra's music could be heard in the background, as if it were a party. We played for an audience that disappeared daily. Our melodies served, also, to cheer the executioners′ work.

The gypsies, or the *roma*, as the Nazis called them, were isolated from the rest of the prisoners. One afternoon we heard shouting. The soldiers were pulling the gypsies out of their barracks, possibly to be taken to the gas chambers, but we watched as they revolted fiercely. They returned the blows; some of the men snatched the arms from the soldiers and shot at them. In the end, the gypsies were massacred. Those of us who witnessed it felt a great admiration for their bravery.

During the speeches that the camp's First Commandant and *Oberstumbannführer* Rudolph Höess pronounced, the orchestra was always by his side. In repeated occasions, I had him very close and looked at him with curiosity. He was kind, somewhat shy and almost harmless. It was incomprehensible to me that such a man, whose appearance was so sensitive, was responsible for the Auschwitz operation and who sent thousands to their death, daily. He loved music, especially baroque. When Höess was exhausted from work, he would approach the orchestra, sit and listen to the music. His favorite piece was *Deutsche Eichen*, the German Oaks, which we had to play time and again for him. He would refer to our group as "my orchestra." Like the rest of the officers, his uniform was always impeccable.

Frequently, Mandel would appear with a request of his, an order rather. We had to prepare to play this or that piece at the following Sunday's concert. He, his wife and his five children always sat in the first row —very Arian and dapper— after attending the officer's mass that each Sunday morning a priest officiated.

That priest, in particular, struck my curiosity. He was tall and blond, seemed friendly and walked in strides without looking too hard anywhere, as if he didn't want to see us and leave soon. I wondered what he thought of the "work" the Nazis were carrying out, of the tortures, of our appearance, of the gas chambers, of the crematoriums and of the undeniable smell of death that floated in that camp. He seemed not to realize what was taking place there.

One morning, while the orchestra played, the trains arrived with a large cargo of French prisoners. Gertrude, our friend from the Paris bakery, was among them and passed by the orchestra. Fritz, her husband, was not with her. I imagined that she'd been transferred from another camp because of her emaciated aspect and her skinniness. We were unable to cross a word. I kept on playing, but my heart raced, about to explode. Sweating and ready to faint, I wanted to run to her and save her. Afterwards, I saw her again, as the soldiers shoved her towards the trucks. Gertrude turned her head and, again, our eyes met, as in a farewell. Powerless and unable to save her, I thought I was going to pass out. She was a good and kindly woman, but old and a disposable object for the Nazis.

A little after Germany's invasion of Hungary, a hundred Hungarian rabbis arrived in the camp, venerable old men with long beards. They were ordered to undress and to dance in a circle before the prisoners, in the middle of the square. They sang the *Kol Nidre*, what we Jews sing before Yom Kippur. I am not sure if the SS knew the meaning of this recited declaration, because they ordered the orchestra to accompany the rabbis while they simultaneously hand-clapped to the rhythm of the music.

When I heard the recitation of "*In the tribunal of Heaven and the tribunal of earth, by the permission of God —praised be He— and with the permission of this holy congregation, we hold it lawful to pray with transgressors,*" I started crying, unable to hold back. How they trampled on our beliefs, our faith! Did we not have the same god? I did not want to look at the rest of the women in the orchestra, but I could hear their sobs. I felt so humiliated, so hurt, ashamed for them and for what was happening to our people. The silence amongst the prisoners was total, but the soldiers were laughing out loud.

*"Blessed art thou, O Lord our God, King of the Universe, who hast preserved us and hast brought us to enjoy this season."*

When the spectacle was over, they were forced to walk naked to the gas chambers. They went, holding their head high, without looking back, until we saw how the doors closed behind them.



That day, they massacred the rest of the newly arrived in two trains, coming from Hungary. The gas chambers and the crematoriums could not keep up with the demand, so they made great piles of bodies and burnt them outdoors. All prisoners were summoned to the central patio and, for hours, we had to witness the horrific scene. The order of the *Endlösung* or "Final Solution" to wipe us out from the face of the earth was being carried out ever more efficiently.

Playing but unmovable on the chair, in vain I tried to escape reality, to vanish into thin air, to ignore what was taking place before me. I closed my eyes not to see, not to feel. I avoided looking at the prisoners so as not to remember their features when I saw them dead. My orchestra colleagues felt the same, pale, tense, about to faint, like myself. The beautiful sounds we produced lightened the infamy.

Two of the orchestra's members committed suicide that night.

*There was talk in the camp about the atrocious experiments Mengele carried out with prisoners in block 10, along with his assistant Kaduch and other doctors. Those who were taken there never returned to the barracks.*

*Ilse told Leah that, on one occasion, she had to accompany a Nazi doctor to Mengele's laboratory to pick some samples. The premises were spotless, aseptic, in contrast to the infirmary where she worked, hardly without medicines or running water. In one wall, there was a collection of human eyes, each pierced through with a pin, as if were a butterfly exhibition. Mengele examined them with care while taking notes and did not bat an eyelid when they walked in.*



*With amputated arms, a women's corpse was lying on what appeared to be an autopsy table. Surgical instruments were placed immediately to the right side, as if someone had left them there temporarily, only to come back and resume the task. Ilse looked carefully and noticed the woman's protruding abdomen. The woman had been pregnant.*

*In one of the laboratory's corners, Ilse observed a bathtub full of little-sized bodies. At first, she thought they were children, but afterwards realized that they were dwarfs, submerged in a liquid that emanated a strong smell. Some had their skin detached from their bones. Stuck to the bathtub was a sign that read: "For the Kaiser Wilhelm Institute, Berlin." Another container, whose contents she was unable to discern, had another sign: Berlin-Dahlem Institute.*

*Mengele liked playing God. He was impervious to the sobs or begging and boasted of being a smart man, whom no one could fool. Even the SS soldiers, experts in cruelty and sadism, feared him.*

*Prisoners arrived from all corners of Europe, so that talk in Russian, Rumanian, Polish, Greek, Italian, and many other languages was a common occurrence. People didn't understand one another easily. Mengele asked for interpreters because it exasperated him that prisoners speak in a language other than German. When they did not understand his orders, he would have them killed immediately.*



*Readily available for his experiments and with a barrack full of children and youngsters at his disposal, he would frequently go and choose himself those he needed for whatever madness that crossed his mind that day. Twins were his favorite and, when they were no longer useful, he would murder them at the same time to afterwards carry out the autopsy and compare them.*

*When a train full of kids arrived —destined to him— Mengele decided to get rid of the majority he had in reserve, who were no longer useful. So, he ordered an enormous group together, had a board nailed at a certain height and then had the children pass underneath. Close to a thousand short kids passed without difficulty and saved their lives. Upon the Nazis' command, the dogs attacked those who did not pass and were then sent to the gas chambers.*

*It was Yom Kippur, when the Jews recite a prayer that says: "The flock must pass under the shepherd's rod, who will decide who shall live and who are to die." Mengele loved to desecrate the Jewish religious rites and would make fun of them. With that action he established who the real boss was: the one to make the flock pass beneath the rod, the one who decided who was to live or die.*

*The orchestra had been formed for some months now, when they placed it before one of the gas chambers from where the process of the selection of the newly arrived prisoners could be seen. They soon understood the routine: at the right those who would remain detained in Auschwitz; to the left those destined for the gas chamber.*

*Placed in the left line, those who insisted on not parting from their relatives would be allowed to join them without knowing that they had chosen death. However, at other times they could reverse the order: to the right death, to the left life. The confusion was evil-intentioned and one never knew what one's fate would be.*

*When the doors to the gas chambers would close, the screams would reverberate terrifyingly. While the women's orchestra played on, they could see the soldier on the roof, with his mask on, inserting the gas cans through the openings. A little after, only silence was left. Meanwhile, in the barracks, the next group was ordered to go and shower, unknowing of their approaching death. The process would repeat itself and the music played on.*

*Some of the* Sonderkommando *prisoners would pull out the corpses covered in vomit, excrement, urine and blood. They would hose them down and, with efficient quickness, open each of the corpses' mouth to extract with a hammer the gold crowns and bridges. They would afterwards check their anus and vagina in search of money, jewelry or diamonds that the dead might have hidden.*

*They would pile the bodies on top of one another, but leave visible the tattooed-numbered arm. To keep a registry of the dead, another brigade would oversee the deed of copying down the numbers, for the Nazis were obsessed with documenting their atrocities with the greatest precision. They would then place the bodies on wheelbarrows and take them to the crematoriums.*

*Some fell during the trajectory. A little later, the black smoke clouds with the stench of burnt flesh invaded everything.*

*In the end, the* Sonderkommando *prisoners were condemned to death. They would be murdered three or four months after having been assigned to that duty, because by then they'd be worn out and seen too much. The first job of those who came to substitute them was to kill them and transport their bodies to the crematorium.*



*Aside from having a terrible and repugnant job, they would be confined to an area apart from that of the prisoners, with whom they were strictly forbidden to have any type of contact. They would often sleep and eat in the crematorium building. They lived in the bowels of hell, with death as their only companion. On some occasions, one of them might come across his wife walking towards death, a father would bump into his son's body, or a son had to incinerate their parents. Many went crazy and would simply end up entering the gas chambers on their own accord, or provoking the guards so these would kill them.*

*Soldiers would often carry out the* sonderaktion *or special actions. First, they would beat up the prisoners, then tie them together, forming a mound of them and then place them over lit wood, douse them in gasoline and burn them outdoors. Still alive, they would writhe in pain and heartrending screams would be heard, while the flames consumed them. They were not only adults, there were also kids. The stench was horrible.*

*Murders went* in crescendo. *By then, the Nazis had extended the lines and the trains rode all the way into the camps. The prisoners' transport was becoming ever more timed and efficient. Human cargo arrived at all hours, which the orchestra received with happy tunes, full of hope. At first, the newly arrived felt reassured and walked with confidence towards their fate. Some of the children skipped and hopped to the music's beat. The women in the orchestra had become pathetic emulators of Hamelin's Pied Piper.*

*Mengele would wait for the prisoners standing in the train platform, as if to welcome them. He hummed a Wagner melody carefree, while his attentive assistants perceived the imperceptible gestures that he made with his hand, head, or eyes. With a kind face and a smile, he would send thousands of people to their death, daily.*



*In the midst of those atrocities and music, Leah felt more and more insensitive, lesser and lesser a human being.*

Witnessing those death scenes produced me a profound revulsion. Through the melody that flowed from the violin, I searched in vain to connect with what once knew and hoped still existed beyond the barbed wire. Fighting against being an accomplice to the degeneracy and cruelty that surrounded me, I didn't want to know who they killed, or want to see their faces because they would become engraved in my memory and would haunt me every day, hours and minutes that I still had left to live. Every fiber in my body wished to dissolve into my own cavity. "Could the world have vanished into thin air? Did nobody care what happened here; no one to come to save us? Had everything disappeared, including goodness?"

One afternoon, we were informed that we had to play for one of the Gestapo chiefs in Poland interested in visiting Auschwitz. Kommandant Höess had thousands of prisoners sent to the gas chambers, in his honor, so that he could prove the gas chambers and crematoriums worked. I will never forget the face of satisfaction on Höess, and the admiration on the visitors while together they observed the black smoke that poured forth from the chimney.



While the orchestra played, Anna's mother and sister went past us on their way to the gas chamber. Anna, without hesitating, dropped her cello and ran towards them. The rest of us didn't know what to do; we didn't dare open our mouths or stop playing. Alma saw this and ran to stop her, but the soldiers had already sealed off the area, and didn't let her through. The doors were open and the group about to enter. Anna turned around, hugging her mother and sister, made a grimace in the manner of a smile and nodded her head, as in a farewell gesture. Alma stood petrified, not knowing what to do. Anna had made her own selection.

The music continued…

For several days, members of the orchestra were unable to talk about what had occurred. Alma was sad, but also held her tongue. I, particularly, felt devastated. Anna was my friend, a sweet young girl, sensitive and with lots of talent. Under other circumstances, she could have managed to fulfill her dream of becoming a soloist. I was certain she had made up her mind much earlier.

Alma named another girl to substitute Anna, but she lacked Anna's virtuosity. I decided that I wouldn't become friend with her, so as not to suffer anymore. A very painful lesson to learn: to survive in this hell, dreaming and laughing was forbidden. It was essential to remain insensible, like a rock, to withdraw into a life of one's own.

During roll call in the main patio, I would sometimes see my sister from afar. As a member of the orchestra, they wouldn't have allowed us to meet, but at least I was relieved to know she was alive. A nightmare I wouldn't have been able to stand, I prayed everyday not to see her headed towards the gas chamber.



One day, Alma took me aside to give a message from Ilse. The soldiers had taken Rachel to work in the officers' club. We all knew that was a brothel at the other end of the camp, out of bounds to the prisoners. My sister had inherited our mother's features and was very attractive, that's why she was chosen. Those who were destined to the brothels never returned. I would no longer have any news from her and it would also be impossible for Ilse to obtain any information. Alma was appalled and I, cornered, powerless before the disaster. On numerous occasions she had asked for a piano so she could reclaim Rachel, but Mandel would always refuse. Cornered, feeling impotent in the middle of total chaos and disaster, I thought I'd go insane.

Desperate and sad, I was depressed for the following weeks. Without having any strength to play the violin and no desire or power to go on, tears would burst from my eyes without my being able to hold them back. Rachel's face kept coming back to my mind, incessantly. Recalling our childhood in Bremen, our little sister rivalries, how much I wished to tell her that I loved her, that she was what was most important to me, to erase anything disagreeable that I might have ever told her! I feared it was already too late.

Getting ready to go to sleep one night, the feared Maria Mandel came in and told me bluntly to follow her. I walked shaking behind her and, to my surprise, we reached the showers. She handed me a deliciously smelling soap bar and a towel, two unthinkable luxuries for a prisoner. She ordered me to quickly take a shower while she'd wait outside. During the shower, I asked myself a thousand times what that woman could possibly want of me.



Scared to death, I followed her down the *lagerstrasse*, the main street that led to the area where the high-ranking SS officers lived, where it was said the Nazis had a bakery, restaurants, a hospital and a pool. The brothel was there somewhere, so I thought we were headed there, that that would be my fate too.

We reached a hut, the entrance guarded by two soldiers dressed in *Waffen* SS uniforms, Himmler's elite guard, in charge of the highest-ranking officers. They wore black uniforms, in the belt buckle a silver death's-head and a red armband with the swastika, surrounded in black trimmings. I had seen them several times bragging arrogantly around the camp. Mandel whispered something into their ear which I was unable to hear and ordered me in. She withdrew, and I found myself in the middle of a luxurious room, bathed in a tenuous light with lovely furniture of which I'd forgotten its very existence. It smelt of fresh fruit.

An ominous feeling of not being alone took hold of me. Then I saw him. There was Mengele, with his back to me, seated in an armchair. He turned around and looked at me for a moment. Not daring to speak and incapable of moving, I felt as if my feet were nailed to the ground.

"What is your name?

"Leah Felton."

"Come close, nothing is going to happen to you," he said amicably.

Very scared, I obeyed. I knew what that man was capable of, as I had heard and witnessed many of his atrocities. Of course, I didn't believe him.

"You're probably wondering what you're doing here, right?"

Unable to utter a word, shaking from head to toe and wanting to vanish that very instant, I nodded.

"You are the best violinist in the orchestra. I have been observing you and know. Play for me, I have been told that this is your violin," he said, while bending down to pull something out from beneath his desk. He handed me the blue case with my Guarneri, which I immediately recognized.

It was unbelievable what was happening to me: the threatening kindness with which that man treated me — whom the prisoners nicknamed the 'Angel of Death'— the return of my violin, his assertion that nothing would happen to me and that all he wanted was for me to play… I was alone with him and that presaged danger.

"So… you are a *mischlinge*," he remarked.

"My father is Jewish and my mother was a Christian," I said.

"You have a sister, right?"

"Yes," I answered while I scrutinized in his eyes the meaning of his question. That man knew everything about me, it was clear. Why did he ask? To confuse me and to fear him even more?

He looked at me with an air of superiority, even with contempt, as someone who is above all. I noticed how a sarcastic smile outlined itself on his face. His attitude changed in an instant as he said with apparent kindness:

"I don't like that horrible uniform they use in the orchestra. When you play for me, I want you to wear the tunic that is on the armchair."



Without a private place to change clothes, I had to undress before him. Since no prisoner wore underwear, I turned around so he could not see me naked. Ashamed, I quickly put on the white tunic, with a ribbon on each side, which pretended to transform the "slave" into a Greek vestal. When that delicate cloth grazed my body, I realized that my skin had forgotten the softness of the garments that I used before, when I was free.

Meanwhile, Mengele looked at me expressionless. He only made an approving gesture with his head as I came close to grab my violin.

"Play," he commanded.

Upon opening the case, I was moved to tears when I read my name in the case's topmost lining, written with dashes of happiness and innocence of another area now long gone. My beloved violin was with me once again! Delicately, I caressed its noble wood. If only Madame Lamar, my music teacher, had seen me at that moment! When she told me that I had talent and that someday I'd play before very important people, not even in her worst nightmares would she'd ever imagined this scene.

As I turned the pegs to tune it, Mengele became impatient. I placed the violin in position, holding the instrument's neck with my left hand and putting my fingers in place. Hardly unable to control my trembling hands and thinking I wouldn't be able to play, I brought the bow to the strings on the bridge.

"Begin," he insisted impatiently.

The room was impregnated of a sweetish aroma of soap, of expensive perfume. Mengele was a refined man, of elegant manners. Now that I could see him up close, I was struck by the delicateness of his hands and was able to confirm, not without satisfaction, that his features were more Jewish than Arian. I almost gave a hint of a smile.



"Don't be fooled, Leah," I told myself. "This man is a devil disguised of nobleness today. Don't be trusting; don't let your guard down." His presumptuous bearing irritated me.

"What do you wish for me to play?" I asked with a barely audible voice, frightened to death.

"Whatever you want," he answered.

I had to be careful not to choose a Jewish composer. That would cost me my life. I decided to play one of the pieces from Schumann's *Fantasiestücke.* I didn't close my eyes for an instant so as not to lose sight of him, just in case, but he seemed inoffensive, motionless in his armchair. In his left hand he held a glass with some liquor in it. He moved his right hand with grace to mark the music beats, as when he sent people on their way to the gas chamber.

The music invaded the silence of those surroundings so alien to my reality, fled out the windows and dissolved into the night.

When I finished my execution, he said:

"The sound of that violin is superior."

"It's a Guarneri," I answered.

"It is a magnificent instrument, indeed. How did it come into your hands?"

"My father bought it for me in Paris."

"Was your father a musician?"

"No, he is a doctor."



"Where is he?"

"I don't know."

"And where is your mother?"

"She died. She was a pianist."

Containing myself so as not to scream to him, I wanted to say: "You people killed her, and possibly my sister and father!" His questions bewildered me. What sort of monster was that man? He enjoyed torturing me.

I chose to perform the *Andante* of Bach's Second Sonata in A Minor in an effort to calm myself down. Mengele then asked for some Chopin, Liszt and Brahms. The despicable Nazi liked the Romantics. Suddenly, he ordered that I change clothes and leave. I tried taking my violin, but he didn't allow me to. He did not get up from the armchair, or said another word.

Shaking from head to toe after coming out of that place, I felt I was going to faint at any moment. One of the soldiers, with the same frozen face as the rest, drove me back with shoves to the orchestra's room. Alma was awake; she seemed to me aware of the reason for my absence. Noticing her relief upon my return, she didn't ask me any questions or made any sort of comment. Some of the women in the orchestra looked at me surprised when they saw me return alone at that hour, nervous and pale. I felt ashamed of what they might think. Perplexed myself about what had occurred, I was amazed to have escaped from the monster's claws.



*On some occasions allied war planes flew close by Auschwitz. The buildings were immense, they could be seen with no difficulty as the planes flew nearby, but only once did they drop some bombs next to Monowitz, where the factories were. Not a single building was damaged. The gas chambers were within reach, as well as the crematoriums and the train tracks were all in plain sight. The prisoners could not understand why it wasn't all destroyed. They no longer cared to die if it meant all that horror would disappear.*

*Four women prisoners managed to steal some explosives from the factories where they worked and gave it to some of the* Sonderkommando *men, who built a rudimentary bomb. They blew up the Crematorium IV of Birkenau and the gas chamber next door. Several SS died in the incident and the murders ceased for some days. As punishment, the women were executed before the firing wall, in front of all the prisoners. Men were also killed and their bodies dragged along the camp's streets.*

*Among the prisoners the rumor circulated that: "The Nazis are invincible, they have made a pact with the devil." "The world doesn't care for us."*

The Mengele incident repeated itself a couple of nights later. Mandel arrived, ordered that I follow her, we'd go to the showers and then we'd head for Mengele's cabin. He, the tunic and my violin were there. I'd change clothes and play for him, who remained mute in his armchair, with a glass in hand. With the other he kept the time.

He had a phonograph in his cabin and hundreds of perfectly ordered records, without a speck of dust, in lovely wooden shelves matching his desk. There was also an upright piano. Hanging in one of the walls stood out a large frame with an oath: "*I, swear to Adolf Hitler, Führer and Chancellor of the Reich, loyalty and valor. I promise obedience until death, to you and the superiors you may have designated. So help me God.*" And below: "*SS Waffen.*" Hitler's portrait was displayed on an opposite wall.



After several weeks of the same routine, he'd order me to stop playing and that I sit before him. Mengele had an incredible collection of ancient music which he bragged about. It was, no doubt, exquisite and attested to its owner's superior knowledge of the genre. We'd listen to Wagner, whom he adored. On one occasion, he gave me a long dissertation on the *Gesamtkunstwerk*, the synthesis of all the arts that the composer captured in *The Ring of the Nibelung*, and several times made me listen to fragments of the piece. I was bored; it was unbearable. On seeing him so euphoric, I thought he saw himself as a Siegfried, the Nordic national hero, Wagner's idol.

"All people must love their music, because that is their essence. When I listen to Wagner's music, I intuit something cryptic, a message that he strives to transmit through his melodies for a new world order," he declared very seriously.

He also told me all in rapture that he and his Führer had attended the famous Bayreuth Festival, founded by Wagner many years back; that he knew Siegfried, his son, in charge of the set designs and orchestration, till his death recently.

He had close ties with his widow, Winifried, a great admirer of Hitler, who remained in charge of the Festival. He would say, proudly, that she was his friend and an unconditional follower of the German regime. His eyes shone on speaking to me of her. I thought that perhaps there was something more between them.



"If he knew that I can't stand Wagnerian chromaticism," I would say to myself, but I didn't dare talk. I felt like a straw doll, mute, rigid, devoid of emotion. Fearing moreover to say something that he'd dislike and that it would awaken the monster within him, silence was my best weapon. Mengele loved to be listened. He must have thought that I was very interested in what he had to say. Stoicism and coldness were my self-imposed rule in that absurd and uncertain game, where any false step would've cost me my life.

On a further occasion he took off on a monologue on the greatness of Dante. In a display of his prodigious memory, he recited entire paragraphs of *The Divine Comedy*, while we listened to the *Dante Sonata* by Liszt, Wagner's father-in-law. He also liked listening to madrigals, based on short lyric poems, in which Dante mixed love with nature.

He fervently admired Goethe. I had to listen to his opinions on Goethe's postulates about the close relationship between music and architecture. "Don't you realize that the great architectonic monuments are pure music, mute, petrified?" he asked me. I didn't know what to answer. I only nodded so as not to antagonize him.

"He's got two personalities," I thought while I listened to him speak. "He is cultured, refined, a music lover, but also a sadist, cruel… a murderer." If anyone happened to see his in the privacy of his cabin, so human, sensitive and musical couldn't believe he was the same man who strolled throughout the camp in his trial by ordeal.

On top of a small table in the corner of the sofa, there was a torchiere with a beige shade resembling patches. In one instance, and with the utmost care and dissimulation, I walked towards the lamp to find out what it was made of. With horror, I saw tattooed numbers. The patches were made from the skin of the prisoners! Undoubtedly, this was a trophy for him. I felt the utmost disgust, contempt and repulsion towards the man.



From the very first moment I was certain that he felt very lonely, even unhappy it seemed to me, but I never understood why he sought my company, a "subhuman and dirty Jew", as the Nazis considered us. "That is why he has me shower before entering his cabin, so that I don't contaminate it," I thought.

While playing in the orchestra, I saw him every day. He would walk around in his white robe, impeccable over his SS uniform. I could not avoid thinking about my father, who was also a doctor, but of the kind really devoted to saving their patients. He, on the contrary, was a devil bearer of death. He ignored me, as if he had never seen me. I, in turn, pretended to be invisible, in the hope he would forget about me.

Mandel would come fetch me several times a week and each time she followed the same routine. On some occasions, she could inform me that Mengele wanted me to prepare a piece for the next time I went to his cabin, like one afternoon that she handed me the score of the *Rondo* of the First Sonata in D Major by Beethoven. I was surprised to find out it was a piece for piano and violin, but I practiced the musical part that concerned me.

That night, as we approached Mengele's cabin, I heard a delicate melody I believed to be Chopin, coming from the piano. Mandel ushered me in and the music stopped. He, as usual, waited seated in his armchair. When my eyes got used to the room's poor lighting, I distinguished a very skinny woman seated at the piano. It was my sister! She was emaciated and seemed very old, but she still had the sweet and pretty face with which father described her. In spite of everything, they'd been unable to wipe out the beauty of her profile.

We looked at each other, unable to speak. Her eyes were immensely sad. I wanted to hug her, tell her so many things, but it was impossible. We were both petrified, on the verge of tears. I felt an enormous happiness knowing she was alive. I supposed that she too. He looked at us immutable, first one, then the other. I could guess, by his sarcastic expression and the evil sparkle in his eyes, that the scene amused him. How could he be such a sadist?

An alarm went off in my head: that night was not like the rest. Something dense, menacing, floated in the air, worse than death's presence. I had a disturbing sensation that something strange occurred. What was my sister doing there? Why did Mengele have her come to his cabin? She had the same white tunic he made me wear. Was it the first time or did he do it often as with me? What lewd game was that man up to? I felt like a hare when it knows it's going to be hunted and has no escape. I tried keeping calm and wait for his instructions. I prayed for him not to hear the fearful beating of my heart. I longed to take my sister by the hand and run out of that place towards freedom, both of us, free. What utopia!

Mengele pointed to the tunic. I knew I had to execute my routine: change clothes and prepare my violin. Rachel remained impassive. She seemed not to understand what was happening either. He made a sign for her to play. When she began, I realized it was Beethoven's *Rondo* that he had also made me prepare. "A concert interpreted by the two sisters," I wondered. A sense of impending danger invaded me.



"You too, play. Don't stop till I tell you," he said bluntly, with a cold, cruel, tone of voice, different from the previous days, which made me shudder. I noticed that night he was wearing a robe.

He closed his eyes, as if enjoying the music. Several minutes later, he got up from the armchair and walked resolutely towards me. He looked me in the eye, as if scrutinizing what I felt. He undid the ribbons of my shoulders and the tunic fell to the ground. Standing naked, in the middle of the room, I considered my options: if I tried defending myself or fleeing, he could kill me and Rachel on the spot. Besides, there were always two armed guards outside.

Frightened to death, I didn't want to look at him, but wanted to chase away the danger and protect my sister. The phrasing of my violin turned into a timbre of confused melodies, dissonant. My entire body shook, my hands sweated, tears rolled down my cheeks, unchecked. Rachel looked at me incredulous, frightened, but kept on playing. Looking at her, I tried to tell her with my eyes not to do anything that would make him furious and worsen matters for both of us. As if fallen into a void, I kept plucking the strings of my violin but could no longer hear the music.

There was a long silence on Mengele's part. I could not see him, but I knew he was very close behind me. I felt his excited breathing against the nape of my neck, his tongue began to slide down my shoulders, leaving on my skin the trail of his saliva, all while he squeezed my breasts with his hands and was pressing his body against mine, in a rhythmic and urgent rub. His hand traveled down my abdomen, slowly but with eagerness and came even closer. He was naked, and his nakedness was burning my skin.



Rachel kept on playing, but was very confused. I looked at her again, to silently beseech her not to come close, no matter what, to stay at the piano.

Mengele stopped, turned around until he was right before me and pulled me towards him with strength. I looked at him imploringly, without daring to open my mouth, in a vain attempt for him to stop, but he didn't move a muscle in his face that now seemed made of stone. His penetrating eyes, fixed upon me, flashed something I hardly recognized, a mixture of hate and lust. Unable to scream or cry, I was paralyzed by fear.

"Stop playing!" he yelled to Rachel. She obeyed and kept motionless seated before the piano, not knowing what to do.

He walked towards the record player and played a Wagner work. I stood still, shaking, naked, in the middle of the room, playing. The violin gave forth a loose, atonic melody.

"You too, enough!" he said, while he came up to me again. He snatched the violin from me and flung it to the ground.

He threw me on the couch, spread my legs, lay on top of me and charged me several times with strength, with the spirit of a conqueror, as an absolute master with all the rights over his slave. His hands clutched mine with strength, so that I could not move. His shortness of breath burnt my cheek and neck. I was torn apart inside. An infinite disgust invaded me. In the background the *Twilight of the Gods* was playing like an ode to my own decadence.



Unable to fight back, I did not have his superior strength or his cruelty, and in no way could beat him. I just laid there, mute, my spirit removed from my body, my eyes fixed on the ceiling, till he finished and got up abruptly. I looked at my sister, who had dropped her head and cried.

"*Raus, raus*!" "Out, out!" he screamed at me, with a bloodshot face, naked, his lust satiated, panting, standing in the middle of the room. I thought he was going to give me a blow or perhaps kill me. In his harsh voice there was both contempt and hate, but not more than that which I felt for him. I got up clumsily, in pain and rage, dressed quickly and went up to where my sister was. Mengele came in-between us and again screamed at me:

"Don't you understand? Are you stupid? *Raus!*"

Mengele grabbed me by an arm and pushed with strength towards the door. I lost my balance and fell to the floor. I looked at Rachel with helplessness; I didn't want to leave her there. She made a sign with the head, with tears in her eyes. Her countenance was one of infinite sadness. Rachel moved her lips without emitting a sound and said: "Leave, please."

"And you, whore, you're staying with me. You're my favorite!" He screamed to my sister. He stood next to her and looked at me defiantly, with a face flushed with rage. Rachel looked at me wild-eyed.

I left in a sea of tears. The soldier looked at me mockingly and took me back to the orchestra's barracks between pushes and shoves. As we moved away from the cabin, little by little, Wagner's shrill music faded, but no one could rid my head of what had happened or the image of my sister, defeated and trapped in the monster's claws.



They had murdered my family in Auschwitz, I'd been subjugated to the most terrible humiliations and now that man took the liberty of taking away from me the last redoubt of my integrity and possess me as if I were some crude disposable object, worthless. And, moreover, he also abused my sister. How I hated him! Him and his people!

That night the moon was absent and a part of me had died.

As always, Alma waited for me. She would not go to sleep until she was sure of my return. She was worried on seeing me arrive so out of shape and weeping.

"What happened, Leah?"

"Nothing," I answered evasive, with a faltering voice. I was ashamed to tell her what had happened. I shook, unable to speak. She looked at my legs from where blood ran down. She extended her arms to hug me and I burst out in uncontrollable tears. Some of the orchestra women witnessed the scene, but said nothing. They no longer had any doubts as to where Mandel took me during the evenings.

Alma took me aside. Like a stream in the middle of unrestrained crying, I vented her everything happened, and that Rachel had stayed behind. Terrified that Mengele would do the same to her or murder her, I felt such disgust! His sticky saliva burnt me, his semen inside me, the coagulated blood… Then and there, I wanted to tear my skin off, to evaporate its smell, but was unable to wash that night since going alone to the showers was forbidden. I could not dispel from my mind his repeated assaults and the humiliation suffered, all before my sister, the danger she ran being there. With my head about to burst, my heart was racing, arrhythmic, tormented by the memory of Rachel, so defenseless in Mengele's claws.

Each night I waited scared to death for Mandel to come and fetch me. The slightest noise made me shudder. I had constant nightmares and could hardly sleep. I planned to kill Mengele, torture him, take revenge, but realized with rage that all that was impossible. The monster never again required my presence.

After trying desperately to get news about my sister, a week later Ilse informed me that she had been taken to the infirmary and that she was very ill, with her bones that seemed to bulge from out of her skin and bruises in her face and body. I was not allowed to see her, despite my pleas and Alma's efforts. The following day, a new message from Ilse informed me that she'd passed away. Even though we were never able to prove it, I was sure that she had been beaten.

I felt guilty for Rachel's death, for my cowardice on not having defended her. Again and again, I reproached myself for not having stood up to Mengele, even though that would have cost us both our lives. Any other calamity would have been preferable for the pain and horrible death she suffered. My loneliness, the guilt I felt for being alive: I had failed my sister. What occurred to us was inhuman, cruel. What had we done to deserve this Calvary? Why was I still alive if my entire family had disappeared? I had lost everything; my life made no sense. I was left alone. Father's words echoed in my head: "You are the strongest, you have to survive." It was not true, I didn't want to survive. I too wanted to die.



That night I contemplated suicide, but Alma must have intuited it because she sat next to me in my pallet and told me persuasively, with affection:

"Leah, all of this will soon end. We must resist a little more; every day we must try to make it to the next. Your life is worth more than all these monsters, don't forget it."

"Why did Mengele take my sister to his cabin? I don't understand… What was his game, Alma?"

"Did you not tell me that he screamed at you that Rachel was his favorite? Are you sure that is what he said?"

"Yes," I answered her.

"Since that night in which you told me what had occurred, I've thought hard about it and think that Mengele —as he has done on other occasions with Jewish imagery and rituals— sought a way to make fun of the Patriarch Jacob. Do you remember the story of Leah and Rachel in Genesis? The Leah in the Bible was the mother of Juda, the trunk from whence six of the twelve tribes of Israel issued. Jesus descended from the tribe of David. Rachel means sheep in Hebrew, the weak one, the submissive one. Perhaps he devised that to defile the Biblical story. You and your sister have the same names as

Jacob's wives. And Rachel was his favorite. That is what made me elaborate this theory. It seems like madness, but one must expect any kind of atrocity from Mengele."

"That man is a sadist. All that is so aberrant... Mengele is crazy."

"It's true, Leah. They all are, and they're blinded by hate. It's better not to think about it. We are better than those savages and deserve to live."



A couple of week later, nausea confirmed what I feared the most. Depressed, alone, I thought I'd go crazy. Like the Leah in the Bible, I would have descendants but not of Jacob but rather of a monster. It could mean a death sentence for me. I told Alma what happened to me before my figure gave me away. She got me a looser-fitting uniform.

*Mengele referred to Jewish women as "whores." During interrogations, he would ask them intimate details about their sexual life. When the trains arrived, he would gather the women and ask which ones were pregnant. Sometimes he would allow for some to give birth to afterwards kill the child in front of the mother and let her live; or he would order for both to be sent to the gas chamber together; or he'd keep the baby to carry out experiments. One never knew what could happen.*

*He would require the* boklovas *to hand him over each month the list of the women who were pregnant. The guardians, the doctors and the nurses were obligated to inform him of the cases that they knew about. When a prisoner informed them that she was pregnant, many thought it as a trap that Mengele had set up to see if they followed orders. Besides those that arrived pregnant, there were also lots of cases of rape in the camp, despite the order given to soldiers of not touching the Jewish women so as not to be "contaminated." The women hid this because it could spell death to them and their babies.*

*Some doctors and prisoner nurses would perform abortions in the barracks in the complicity of dawn. First, they would stuff a cloth in the woman's mouth so that she wouldn't scream. Meanwhile, several women held her down, stripping her membrane to induce labor. If the baby was born alive, they would drown him in a bucket of water. In any case, the children had no chance of survival in those infrahuman conditions. It was a cruel act, but a necessary one. The prisoner would go out to work the following day and the Nazis would not discover what had occurred.*

*When Mengele found out what was taking place behind his back, he made all the women file by naked. It was a gruesome scene, surrealistic, to see them with their uniform in hand and a shaved head, subjected to the almighty's scrutiny.*

*Inevitably, the bulge in her belly would always give her away...*

I rejected that fruit of evil which germinated within me. When I began to feel the creature's movements, I wondered if they would allow it to live and if someday I would feel love for that child.

How lonely I felt and how much I needed my mother by my side during those months! I fantasized about the circumstances being different: that Auschwitz only be a bad dream, that my parents and sister be alive and by my side, that the father of my child be someone else and that we'd been in love. But the cruel and undeniable reality imposed itself and went more insane by the day.

*Mengele would spend hours bent over the microscope in search of the genetic code to create a superior race and multiple childbirths. Everyone knew his fascination for twins and dwarfs. When the trains arrived, he would order the* Sonderkommandos *to ask the prisoners if there were twins and to promise them preferential treatment. The parents would order their kids to go up to him and tell him:* "Wir sind zwillinge!" "*We are twins*!" *Mengele, with a smile, would stroke their head with tenderness and take them under his wing.*



*If a blond baby with blue eyes arrived at the camp or was born there, he would isolate it to "Germanize" him or her. Those who had dark hair and eyes, he almost always killed immediately. If it befitted him, he would inject the children's eyes to see if it was possible to change their color. Block 10, his private laboratory, was always well-stocked with guinea pigs that he tortured at his will in the name of science.*

*Dwarfs were sent to a special barrack, apart from the rest of the prisoners. On one occasion, a large family arrived from a circus in Ukraine. Seven were dwarfs. Mengele was fascinated. He carried out experiments with each one of them, until he killed them all.*

Among the orchestra women none knew how to provoke an abortion. I tried speaking to Ilse so she would help me out, but it was not possible because prisoners not belonging to the group were not allowed to come to our dormitory. Besides, the procedure had to take place at dawn so the Nazis would not learn about it.

"In any case I mustn't become fond of this child. They will murder it as they do with most children or, in the best-case scenario, they will take it away from me. Besides, it will be a monster, like its father, who is the embodiment of evil," I thought over and over.



As I always played seated, I could conceal my state. I thought that if I wasn't murdered at that time was because Alma protected me. When the first contractions began, she asked —almost ordered— the *boklova* to take me to the infirmary, because she was not allowed to accompany me. That was meant to be the happiest moment in a woman's life and all I wanted was to die.

Ilse, forewarned by Alma, managed that I be transferred to a hospital because complications arose with the delivery. Horrified, I learned I had delivered twins. They were not identical: one had dark hair and brown eyes close together; the other light reddish-brown hair and blue-eyed. "The monster was going to celebrate," I thought. Right after the babies were born, I was only able to see them briefly. Mengele, who was immediately informed, shortly thereafter walked into the hall all excited to see the twins, the first to be born in Auschwitz. I heard him say:

"Finally, twins are born in this place!"

Even though he pretended not to know me, I was certain he knew I was the mother. He only said out loud, with a hint of contempt:

"It's incredible that such perfect creatures be the sons of a filthy Jew."

Understanding that he had allowed me to live till that moment to cap off his plan to torture me, I feared for the babies. Mandel was present, looked at me with derision and almost burst out laughing.



Mengele ordered for the children to be taken away. I can't say that I cared. Besides being dazed, I felt embarrassment, disgust, horror. What I had turned into that I didn't want my kids? As a young child I had dreamed excitedly of the day that I'd become a mother. Now everything was different. Was my hate for Mengele stronger than the supposed maternal love that all women must feel? Hours later, I was sent back to the barrack. I walked back there like an automaton, surprised to still be alive.

I continued in the orchestra, but my execution became mechanic, insensitive, like myself. My sonorous world had become a deaf recitative, progressively scarier. I plucked the violin chords, but it no longer felt the same. A harrowing emptiness dwelt within me, as I could not hear the music.

Ilse found out that Mengele was delighted with his twins. He had a German nurse caring for them and the cribs were in the room next to his laboratory, where he could watch over them closely.

For days, we had been noticing unusual movements among the soldiers; they were nervous, unconnected to their routine. It was rumored that the Nazis were losing the war, but we thought it unbelievable because we had come to think that they were invincible. The tension among the prisoners was unbearable. One morning, a large prisoner cargo arrived from Poland from the ghetto of Lodz. They were practically all sent to the gas chambers. The crematoriums were running at full capacity for several days and the stench saturated the camp.

A little later, the women's orchestra was dissolved and we were sent back to the common barracks along with the rest of the camp's prisoners. There was a rumor circulating that a great number of women would be transferred to the Bergen-Belsen Camp. Days before departure, Alma fell gravely ill. Mengele gave the order for her to be taken to hospital, but she died two days later of an intestinal infection. In truth, the cause of death was never established, but rumor had it that she'd been poisoned.



The orchestra members improvised a funeral for her. I played a melody from Brahms' *Ein deutsches Requiem* in her honor, while the rest stood with bowed heads. Up to then Alma had saved us from death and we felt indebted to her. Mandel was present at the funeral, but two days later disappeared, as well as many of the *boklovas* and women guards, among them Irma Grese. It was rumored that they had fled before the imminent defeat.

Gas chambers now operated frenetically day and night. The crematorium's chimneys sent forth a fetid, putrefying smoke. It seemed they were intent on murdering all the prisoners. The scarce food that they gave us became even scarcer. Mengele no longer exhibited himself as before. It was said he was confined to the laboratory.

At my request, Ilse tried to find out how the twins were doing and if there was a way of my seeing them before I was murdered or sent somewhere else. Feeling like a monster, I needed to know if some degree of tenderness or love awoke within me; wanted to see in their traits if they were mine. Ilse was informed that one had died, and that the other continued under Mengele's strict custody, who did not allow for anyone to come close to him.



Immediately, the following day, hundreds of us women prisoners left for Germany in a smelly train, with no seating and windows covered with wooden strips, like the one which brought us to Auschwitz. Ilse bribed a *kapo* with some medicines so she could sneak into the wagon where I'd be traveling. We melted in an embrace the minute she came on board. We were together once more. When we began moving away, we were surprised to see through the cracks how the soldiers had thrown open the main gate and were forcing out thousands of prisoners, pushing them with the butt of their weapons. It was dreadfully cold, it had snowed and the road was white. Those undernourished specters, hungry, with a faltering step, weak, without the adequate clothing and many barefoot, would not resist. It was a death sentence.

Enormous smoke columns spewed from the crematoriums, scattering throughout the sky. We could hear the explosions that came from Auschwitz. The Nazis were trying to erase their deeds. Something strange happened, the self-proclaimed gods dispersed. They were not invincible as they led us to believe. "They will have to kill us all. Those of us traveling on this train are witnesses to their horrors, and someone will survive and give account of what happened," I thought.

The trip lasted two days, again with no food or water, the windows walled up, with only one bucket to relieve our needs.

In the carriage we traveled in, thirteen women died. We reached Bergen-Belsen on the verge of collapse. We no longer formed part of the orchestra there, nor did we have those basic privileges that had helped us survive in Auschwitz. Infested with lice and fleas, the guards did not allow us to leave the barracks, hardly giving us any food or water. Overcrowding was terrible. Most of the prisoners suffered gastroenteritis, the latrines had overflowed and many lacked the strength to rise from their cots. The stench was unbearable, causing us nausea and severe vomiting.

Hundreds died daily from hunger, diseases and, especially, from typhus, which had become endemic. We were stupefied, bestialized, as if alien to what occurred to us. Catatonic, we didn't think, we didn't reason. We only waited for death staring into the void.

One April morning we heard voices, people screaming running from one place to another and the deafening sound of tanks. Our weakness prevented us from seeing what was happening. Then a woman poked her head into our barrack and said:

"The war is over; the war is over. We are free!"

English soldiers entered Bergen-Belsen and the Nazis surrendered without a struggle. Days later, they found dynamite charges scattered through the camp. The Nazis confessed that on the day of liberation they were going to carry out the order they'd received to destroy everything, prisoners included. Once again, we'd outwitted death.

At one end of Bergen-Belsen, the liberators found more than ten thousand bodies —naked and decomposed corpses of adults and children piled on top of one another— that the Nazis hadn't had the time to disappear. That image will never be erased from my memory. Swarms of flies flew above them. The English forced the Nazi soldiers to dig graves to bury the corpses, but there were so many and as the days passed the bodies kept decomposing, that immense excavators were brought in and they were buried in common graves. The stench of putrefaction and death remained floating in the air.



To our surprise, we were informed that the transfer of the orchestra members to Bergen-Belsen had been ordered by Maria Mandel before her departure from Auschwitz. She drove us out of there because she knew they intended to kill all the prisoners. With this last act she saved almost all of our lives. Was there some trace of humanity or remorse? We'd never know the answer.

We were in our bones, hungry, emaciated. The English soldiers were astonished to see so many undernourished and sick people. It occurred to them to give us canned meat, bread and chocolate bars. In their desperation, the prisoners chocked with the food. Ilse warned us:

"Don't eat that, don't touch the food, our stomachs won't tolerate it. Chew small portions, slowly, very slowly, take small sips of water."

Very few heeded her warning. They immediately began having terrible stomach aches with uncontrollable diarrhea and hundreds died. In any case, I couldn't eat. I'd become used to being hungry and hardly had the will to move. I think that is why I survived.

The English soldiers were kind. They treated us as human beings, with dignity and respect, got us up on our feet and helped us walk. For the first time in a long time, someone in uniform who did not pose a menace took care of us, without shoving or screaming at us. Shortly after, dozens of doctors and nurses swarmed in with equipment and medicines and set up a hospital.

We started bathing every day. They brought clothes and shoes from the warehouse and, for the first time in a long time, we could dress in something other than a prisoner's uniform. We were installed in the Nazis' dormitories, which were immaculate, comfortable, with clean beds, sheets and blankets. They torched the filthy barracks to wipe out the typhus epidemic which threatened to do us all in. Witnessing the event with incredulity, those of us who had managed to survive till then were very weak and hardly had any strength to celebrate.

The cleanliness, the order and the absence of foul smells were strange to us. Once again, we had to learn how to use soap and a toothbrush, to sleep in a bed, to wear undergarments, to change clothes, to eat, to use cutlery, to express our ideas freely, to laugh. We felt alien towards those routines which were normal and matter-of-fact to any human being.

During the following days, thousands of refugees came in from other camps. The English would pick up those they found wandering aimlessly on the roads. They also came with dead bodies that the Nazis were forced to carry and cremate. "A sweet revenge... Now they don't have the *kapos* to do their dirty work," I thought.

When I was told I was free, my first reaction was to go as far as possible, but rather decided on returning to Auschwitz as soon as I felt a little stronger. My initial intentions were to find father alive, to recover my son, and to put my feelings to the test to verify if there was any kindness left in me that the Nazis hadn't snatched.



Horrified when I came across my starved image reflected on a mirror, my face was lined with wrinkles, opaque eyes trapped in two dark sockets, my hair thin, dry and lifeless, sallow skin, hunched over. Unable to recognize myself, where was the Leah I knew? Not only hadn't I changed inside, I looked like a cadaverous old woman while barely 23 years old.

*In Auschwitz, like in most concentration camps, the SS forced the prisoners out on the Death March to vacate them. They tried to erase their atrocities: many crematoriums, gas chambers and cells were torched or blown up.*

*Weak in the extreme, without coats, water or food, in the middle of a frost, the majority didn't resist. At the end of January 1945, when the Soviets entered Auschwitz, they came across thousands of corpses strewn along the roads and nearby fields. Inside the train carriages which were stationed in the platform they found thousands of bodies, one on top of the other, dead from asphyxia. In their flight, the Nazis did not open the doors. It was never found out whether this was done or purpose or they just plain forgot.*

*The Soviets carried out, in their turn, many atrocities: rapes, murders and plundering in Auschwitz and in the surrounding areas. A contingency of the United Nations —along with the*

*Allies— arrived several days later. Some of the concentration camps were turned into hospitals and into refugee camps. The work of physical and mental rehabilitation began for the victims, as well as family reunifications, which would take years.*



Morally destroyed and still weak, two weeks later Ilse and I set out for Auschwitz. Despite the English's attempt to dissuade us, we were so determined that they got us a transfer to Prague in a passenger train. A collection was made to provide us with some money and food for the trip, which somewhat renewed our faith in mankind. What awaited us wasn't going to be easy. We'd still have to cross Germany to reach Poland and the times were chaotic.

The train was packed. We were struck by the cleanliness of the carriages. It traveled very slowly and made several stops. When we reached Pilsen, in Czechoslovakia, we decided to step out onto the platform. That freedom to do whatever we pleased seemed strange. Our malnourished aspect must have stood out, because people asked us where we were coming from and the meaning of the tattoo in our arm. When we answered that we'd been in a concentration camp, they didn't understand what we were talking about. They even went as far as to ask us why we had not stayed there. A man with contempt said: "Return there, we don't want Jews here, we don't need them."

On the verge of tears, Ilse and I quickly headed back to the train. Were we really free, or were we still prey to hate and incomprehension? We didn't speak for the rest of the trajectory, I don't know if out of indignation or sadness.

When the train was about to take off, someone leaned into to our carriage and screamed the news: "Hitler has committed suicide!" People reacted in a murmur. Ilse and I looked at each other incredulous. "He was not invincible, after all," we both thought, bur didn't dare express our joy. A lot of Nazis could be on the train.



In Prague we had to change trains to reach Krakow. The available transport was scarce and the money that we had left over from the collection by the English was not enough for the journey. We were at the station for two days straight, almost without eating or drinking water. Finally, in the middle of the confusion, we managed to slip past the authorities and sneak into a train headed to Poland. The man in charge of ticket collection realized the deplorable state in which we were and pretended not to notice us. That's how we reached Krakow.

The journey to Auschwitz was even worse. We had to do the entire trajectory on foot. Roads were impassable and there were still occasional bombardments. We heard shots in the distance, but were unable to tell how far away or where they were coming from. We came across loads of corpses on the side of the road and very weak people, with blank stares in their eyes, dragging their feet clumsily to go nowhere. It looked like a slow-motion horror film.

Military convoys rolled through the road. When we heard the noise of the motors, we ran to hide. Sometimes we cut across the country to avoid pathways, but that wasn't safe either because many Nazis were hiding in the countryside, killing the Jews they came across. There could also be partisans, of the Resistance, who shot anything that moved.

We continued onwards, even with the uncertainty of not knowing where we were and how much longer till we reached our destination. There was no one to ask. At that moment they all looked like enemies. The peasants would turn us away, closing their doors in our faces. We couldn't believe we produced fear in them or that they still harbored that unexplainable hate. When they told us "out, Jews," I wondered if they realized that Hitler was dead and the Nazis defeated. The effects of hatred continued. Only in two occasions we were welcomed with generosity and their meager food was shared with us.



Since leaving Bergen-Belsen, it took us two weeks to get to Auschwitz, by now taken over by the Allies. The camp was unrecognizable, much cleaner and orderly. They'd turned it into a great hospital to look after the prisoners they found or those they picked off the roads and who were too weak to be transferred elsewhere. They looked like specters, in their bones, without muscles, deformed from malnutrition, with their skin parchment-like and full of sores: ghosts out of a horror picture, just like Ilse and me.

Prisoners were desperate to know the whereabouts of their relatives. Allied authorities wrote down their information to try and help them and reunify families, but within that chaos it seemed like an altogether impossible job. There were no kids left in Auschwitz. Contrary to the Nazis, for whom children were disposable, the allies had given them priority and they were almost all sent with their surviving family or foster families.

Because the Nazis had the sick habit of documenting all their actions, the birth of my children would likely appear as the only twins that were born in the camp, as well as the death of one of them. There was no trace of the surviving one. I was informed that, with all certainty, he probably must have died as well since there was no record. Undoubtedly, it had occurred during the Nazis' last days. In those uncertain times, many documents had disappeared and inaccuracies were frequent.



We were told that Mengele had escaped one night, shortly after our transfer to Bergen-Belsen. No one knew where he was. My violin and my kid had also disappeared. In my head hovered the possibility of his having taken my child, to raise him like an Arian.

After lots of searching, I was informed that father's name appeared in the lists, with the annotation that he'd been sent to Dachau, in Germany. The hope of finding him alive produced lots of joy in me, but months later his death was confirmed.

My two years spent in Auschwitz meant centuries for my spirit. I urgently needed to begin anew. I would have to bury my failed love of mother, the grief of having lost my entire family and the certainty that very little was left of me. We didn't want to return to Germany, where there would be many Nazi collaborators. We could not imagine our reaction if by chance we bumped into some Auschwitz guards on the street or in a shop. Besides, where were those who proclaimed their hate for the Jews, who had painted signs, who'd beaten up our people and applauded the Nazis? Unpunished and free, no one called them to account.

Neither did I have strength to return to Bremen. Unable to carry out the idea of finding my house without my parents or my sister, I decided it was a chapter in my life to leave behind. Germany was my homeland, but I'd never return. The Leah from before no longer existed. They had turned me into another person; someone I didn't like.

They gave us medical treatment for a week, but we wanted to leave. We couldn't stand that horrible, place full of memories, and asked to be sent to Paris as soon as possible in the transport assigned for the prisoners. Refugees from all over the place arrived daily and those very same trains would take those who were headed to the different European cities.

The train we traveled in was clean, with seating, open windows and a toilet. The carriage was full of the dregs of mankind, but hardly a murmur was heard. We carried the guilt of being alive on our shoulders, a lacerating pain that would follow us forever. We were free, but no one spoke loudly, no one dared to laugh. The collective solitude was overwhelming. The smell of hell still floated among us, it was impregnated in our soul. We could still feel on our skin the ashes of the dead, our dead. It seemed as if we were destined to be banished from happiness.

When we moved away from the Polish countryside, I closed my eyes. Freedom and the landscape's beauty wounded my retinas. The image of our front room in Bremen came to mind: Rachel dressed in a lovely green dress seated at the piano and I, by her side, about to perform with her with my violin. Our parents looked at us from one end of the room. We began playing, but the scene took place in utter silence. I was desperate because I couldn't hear the music. Little by little a distant melodic phrasing emerged, a melody of confused timbres, first very tenuous, then stronger, unstoppable...

*Thaïs' Meditation*. I liked it so much, that Rachel bestowed on me as *Leah's Meditation*.

My heartbeats were becoming more intense, to the rhythm of percussion, with an offbeat allegro. Rachel stood up from the piano and placed herself next to mother and father. All three kept looking at me while I played my Guarneri. Their shapes blurred till they disappeared. The music vanished very slowly with the breeze that grazed my face.

I opened my eyes and looked at the lovely landscape. A pleasant sensation of peace invaded me, hearing an inner voice that said:

"Leah, you are alive! Music has returned to your life!"

# Fourth Movement – *Adagio*

Alex took the document Mariana handed him and held it in his hands for a moment, as if hesitating to read it. He would finally know the truth, his dreaded truth. "Newborn male, believed to be five months old, born in the Camp of Auschwitz, Poland, of unknown parents, presumably dead. The adopted parents: Henry and Amelia York, residents of Washington, DC, United States of America." The adoption, which took place in Munich, had been registered in the United States State Department in May 1945."

Nora looked at him sadly. "The war kids… forty years later they still feel the ravages of that catastrophe. Poor man," she thought. Discretely, she left the office to prepare three cups of tea. She too needed one.

Clouded in tears, Alex's face reflected all the anguish which had not abandoned him since he first held in his hand that other document discovered in his parents' house.

Scenes of his childhood burst into his mind: the first bicycle his father bought him and his mother's warning to be careful; the day he began his music lessons, his upright piano and then the grand piano that was given to him as a surprise gift when he turned thirteen; the patience with which his mother waited for him while in music classes; his first concert; when he won the Van Cliburn Competition and saw his parents seated in the first row, beaming, swollen with pride; his mother's tenderness and understanding, confidant and friend in his first romances; how happy they were when he married Mariana and then their sadness when he divorced; the wise advice and the love lavished on him.



How could he have suspected that they were not his real parents? Why hadn't they told him? He would have loved them all the same, perhaps even more. "Now that I know, how much I wish they were alive to thank them for what they did for me," he thought.

"It's me… It's me… I knew it," he said crestfallen, in a whisper. Mariana caressed his hands.

Nora returned with the tea and sat before them.

"What else can we do, Nora? I need to know all the truth." Alex asked with anxiety showing in his face.

"In the Archives we have addresses, telephones and places of employment of a great number of people who were interned in Auschwitz. We always ask them to inform us if they change addresses so we're able to locate them in case someone comes to us looking for them, like you now. This manner has proven effective in reuniting many families. Something is certain, though: you were one of a couple of twins, so that incident could not have gone unnoticed due to the importance the Nazis placed on twins. If you allow me, I will call a friend of mine —who was also here during the same time I was and worked in the hospital— and ask her if she knows anything about the birth of some twins."

"Please do so," Alex said.

"My friend is presently at work, so I'll call her in the evening. If she gives me any reliable lead, I will try to dig up more information. I suggest you both go to your hotel and rest. You've been here for days, and emotions have been intense. Come back tomorrow afternoon. Something more solid should have transpired by then. You have my word I'll do everything in my power to help you."



"Thank you, Nora. This means a great deal to me."

"Certainly, Alex, you're welcome."

"Let's go to have lunch and go for a walk around Krakow. We both need to wind down and talk for a while," Mariana suggested to Alex.

Grateful and thanking her again for her assistance, they said goodbye to Nora.

***

Alex and Mariana went to a small restaurant in the city's square. In a corner was a mime, on the other side a man playing the accordion, a group sang, a woman made impersonations. The multitude moved like a swarm all over the place. Alex, with a serious face, hardly spoke. Mariana also felt heartbroken and tried in vain to find a way of cheering him. She felt sorry to see him so tormented. He looked at her for a while in silence, took her hands and confided:

"Without you this would have been unbearable. Thank you for being by my side and for all your help. You are the most important thing in my life. I made a terrible mistake in having given my career priority and neglecting our marriage. We could try once more. Would you remarry me?"

Mariana looked at him moved. How foolish was he; she had never ceased loving him. And only know did he realize it?

"A lot would have to change, Alex. Your selfishness, your absences, that loneliness I found myself in, totally excluded from your world and observing how our relationship ended... It took me a long time to heal and now, finally, I live in peace with myself. I'm apprehensive that history would repeat itself."



Believe me Mariana everything will be different this time around. Time has gone by; we're both more mature now. Besides, I've reflected on what happened and take full responsibility for our marriage's failure. Please forgive me for all the suffering I put you through. I was a self-centered idiot; it won't happen again. From now on, I'll limit my concert appearances and will make the proper adjustments in my career. I love you. Please let me make you happy and grow old with you. We both deserve that opportunity.

"I love you too, Alex. I will not deny it. I have also thought a lot about this. You are right, we deserve a second chance, but first we must find your truth, find your parents, and return to the normal rhythm of our lives. We have a lot to talk about and straighten out between us, but the most important has already been said."

Alex nodded and stood watching her with tenderness. He smiled for the first time in many days. Approaching her, he kissed her, and she kissed him back.

That evening, Alex spent the night in Mariana's bedroom.

Next day, during breakfast, they talked for a long time. They conjectured on what Nora's new investigation could uncover and made plans, as a couple, for the future. Alex felt happy, as if he were reborn, in spite of it all. He repeated again and again how much he loved her and Mariana reciprocated. They went for a stroll along the banks of the Vistula and had a light lunch at Wawel Castle's café, before a lovely panorama of the city of Krakow. It was time to return to Auschwitz. Both were anxious.



Nora waited for them, optimistically. She had some promising news.

"I spoke with my friend last night and she confirmed that, indeed, there was only one birth of twins in the camp a little before the Nazis fled. She does not recall the exact date, but she believes it was towards the beginning of December in 1944. Two boys, she informed me. It created quite a stir in the hospital.

"In December of 1944… In other words, in May of 1945 the children would have been five months old as confirmed on the adoption certificate, correct?" Alex pondered out loud.

"Alex, please allow Nora to finish her story," Mariana interjected.

"My friend was not present at the delivery, nor did she get to see them. Neither does she recall the name of the prisoner who informed her about the birth of the twins, but she did mention that the mother was a very young girl, one of the members of the women's orchestra, a violinist. I asked her to call me if she recalled anything else."

"A violinist..." Alex repeated in an undertone, as in a reflection.

"Was there a women's orchestra in Auschwitz?" Mariana asked surprised.

"Yes, as well as several other men's orchestras. Don't forget that the Nazis were very musical..." she said with irony.



"Will it be possible to get information on the orchestra's violinists?" Alex asked.

"I already followed-up. I went through the archives, especially at the time my friend said the birth of the twins took place, to find out how many violinists were there. Luckily, the list of the orchestra members is pretty complete. The women's one, which is the one that interests us, was created after the men's and lasted over two years. It was dissolved a little before the camp's liberation. I remember seeing them and hearing them play. It was a very select group who had some privileges. The one who organized and directed the ensemble was a famous Austrian violinist. I believe she was the niece of Gustav Mahler."

Not knowing what to say and each absorbed in their own thoughts, Alex and Mariana remained silent, holding on to every word Nora said.

"Here are the eight names of the orchestra's violinists. Luckily, we have a registry of each one of them. The five who appear as deceased were already older at that time. Not too long ago I heard of two others and, from personal circumstances, they cannot be the person we are looking for. There is one, Leah Felton, who back then was very young. She appears as a resident of Amiens, a village not too far from

Paris, but it is information from many years back. We don't have her current address or any other information."

"It can't be... so close to Paris, where you have been living for years now," Mariana said astonished.

"Amiens is a small village. It's possible that it won't be so hard to find her," Alex added.



A secretary walked into the office to inform Nora that she had an important phone call. She excused herself to take the call and returned a few minutes later.

"That was my friend with whom I spoke last night. She remembered the name of the other prisoner who also worked in the infirmary and who was friends with the mother of the two children: Ilse Babish. We must presume this woman knows the entire story. I have asked my assistant to immediately look for all her information; to see if we have anything that could help us."

"Will there be available any information regarding the children's father?" Alex inquired.

"We never have that information. I am sorry I am unable to help. There were very few births in the camp, for you must remember that the Nazis would kill the children, except in rare occasions. But, if you can find the mother, she no doubt will be able to answer that question," Nora responded.

Alex needed some fresh air and left the office for a while. Nora took advantage of the opportunity to speak to Mariana, in private.

"I didn't want to mention this in front of Alex, but many of the pregnancies resulted from rapes by soldiers in the camp. Though forbidden from touching the prisoners, they very often disobeyed that order."

"Do you think that might have been the case?" asked Mariana.

"It's possible. I don't know how we could prepare Alex for this eventuality. Of the registered births, which were not many, the father's name never appears, as if it didn't matter. I guess this was meant to hide the soldiers' actions."



The conversation between the two women was interrupted when Alex returned to the salon. Mariana was disconcerted and very nervous before the possibility they could be faced with and Alex's reaction. "It will be very painful for him if his father turns out to be a Nazi!" she thought.

Shortly thereafter, the assistant entered with a document in her hand and gave it to Nora, who remained pensive for a while.

"There is something curious here. We have an address for Ilse Babish and it says that she also resided... in Amiens, but it's more than twenty years old. It's the only thing we have of hers. I don't know if it'll be of any help," Nora said.

"It can't be a coincidence. It's possible that they kept up a relationship throughout the years," Mariana remarked.

"Under those atrocious circumstances, it was frequent for bonds of friendship to develop between prisoners. When one loses everything and everyone, she usually grabs on to whoever offers affection, especially if that other person can understand her miseries. It's very probable that those two women lost their families and ended up alone, like it happened to so many. I agree with Mariana, I don't think it's a coincidence. Perhaps they're good friends. Ilse must know where Leah Felton is. You must go to Amiens."

"We must find them!" Mariana reiterated.

"If they're still alive," Alex said anxiously.

Nora felt satisfied because, at least in this case, she had found information that was helpful. It wasn't always like this. Many a time she had to face the pain and frustration of those who didn't find their loved ones. She wished them both luck, although she was still apprehensive as to what they might discover. As been witness to a lot of war stories could be terrible.



Finally, Alex and Mariana had hope, a reliable lead. That woman, Ilse Babish, must know the truth and the whereabouts of Leah Felton, if she was still alive. Deciding to leave and look for her as soon as possible, they bid farewell to Nora and Mr. Rosenback, not without first thanking them for their invaluable help and promising to let them know about their findings.

The following morning, they took an early flight to Paris and headed to Amiens in the afternoon. The village was, sure enough, quite small. They found the address that Nora had given them without too much trouble. The woman who occupied the house had been there for fifteen years and didn't remember any Ilse living there. Nevertheless, she took them to a neighbor who had lived in the locality her entire life.

"Yes, I remember Ilse," she remarked, "her husband was French and had two boys who were very well-mannered. They were good people, very quiet. They moved a long time ago and I never heard from them again."

"Don't you remember a friend of hers by the name of Leah Felton?"

"No, Ilse and I weren't friends. We only said hello in the mornings, on her way to work."

"Ilse worked?" Mariana interjected.

"Of course, she was a nurse at the Saint Esteban Hospital. It's five or six blocks away from here."

They thanked her and headed towards the hospital. Some remembered Ilse, but the youngest didn't know who she was because for years she no longer worked there. One of the nurses referred them to the Director, Dr. Lemonnier, who had been at the hospital for thirty years.

"Why are you looking for Ilse Babish?" the Doctor inquired.

"In truth, we are looking for is a friend of hers, Leah Felton, and we would like to ask Ilse where we can find her. It's regarding a very important and urgent matter. Here is my card, I am Alex York, pianist. She is my girlfriend, Mariana Arroyo."

"Ilse worked with me for several years and we are fond of one another. She comes around here sometimes, but I must look for her phone number. I will call you tomorrow to inform you if I was able to come up with it."

On his way back to his office, he stopped and said:

"Leah Felton, the violin professor? Yes, I saw her several times she came to meet Ilse when this one would finish work."

Alex and Mariana looked at each other, surprised at their good luck. They were nearing the truth. Going back to the hotel, the sun began to set and the afternoon cooled down.

***

That night they went out for dinner and had a long conversation. The relationship between them flowed as if the years hadn't gone by. A new connection was established, more mature and understanding than before.

"Mariana, it scares me to know who my father was. I have thought a lot about it, and sometimes have the urge of not going any further with this investigation."

"Why do you say so?"

"Such a young woman that comes out of a concentration camp and who apparently had been a prisoner for some time… Those children could not have been the product of love."

"I felt the same way but didn't dare mentioning it to you. Nora also hinted at that possibility."

"On the other hand, I am very anxious to meet Leah Felton and ask her if she is my mother, like we believe. Besides, although afraid of facing the truth, I also want to know everything about my father."

"Do you think she'll tell you?"

"I hope so, even if I have to beg her to do it. It's something that tortures me. I have the right to know, don't you think?"

"And, if as we fear, he turns out to be a Nazi, what would you do?"

"I can't answer that with certainty. It would be horrible, but it's a possibility that I would have to accept and deal with. Could he be still alive?"

Mariana looked at him with compassion. Alex was disconcerted; his face showed profound pain.

Upon returning to the hotel, they found a message from Dr. Lemonnier, advising them to come to the hospital in the morning.

Alex was unable to sleep that night. Very soon he'd know the truth and it frightened him. He felt a desire to flee, to not meet his biological mother and to not go further into his father's identity and into the terrifying details of his birth. "Who am I in truth?" he wondered over and over.

Mariana, too, had a sleepless night. "Poor Alex, his world has come crumbling down. The death of his parents, finding out that he was adopted. How will he face all this? How could I possibly help him?"

They rose early and, in a hurry, headed to the hospital. They waited impatiently at the reception area. Several minutes later, the Director came up to them and, kindly, handed them a piece of paper.

"Here's Ilse's telephone number and address. I already spoke to her. You can go visit her, as she is waiting for you. She doesn't live far from here."

***

"Hello Leah, are you going to be home? I need to talk to you."

"Yes, I am not going out. Today I only had one student and I am free in the afternoon. What's the matter Ilse?"

"I'm on my way. I need to talk to you, but don't worry."

Leah hung up the phone. "My dear friend Ilse, always by my side... What could she be up to? Surely she wants to talk about something. At least she has her own family, her husband, her children," she thought.

Just turned sixty-one, Leah contemplated at herself in the mirror. "You're not that bad-looking for your years, in spite of it all," she said to herself. Her face was lined with wrinkles but, in her short and curly chestnut-colored hair, there was hardly any grey. Her small brown eyes and her father's unmistakable Jewish nose gave her a vivacious face. She didn't consider herself beautiful, like her sister, but people said she was an interesting woman.



Having time for the rest of the day, Leah went to her studio to practice the violin for a bit. How far away was that dream of hers of being a soloist! Looking at her fingers, sore from the slave work, she now remembered that day ages ago… It was shortly upon arrival in Amiens when she realized that she and her hands were not the same. They lacked the innocence to produce the pure sound of music. Realizing and facing the harsh reality at the time, Leah buried her dream.

Josef Felton's words came back as an evocation when he bought her the Guarneri: "When I see you debuting on stage and proudly applaud you, I will know this enormous effort was worthwhile." That never happened. Her father, her violin and her yearnings had disappeared for good in the middle of the horror. All that she had left was the tattoo, those damned numbers forever engraved in her arm.

It was then she had the certainty that the Leah from before would never return and decided to completely immerse herself into teaching children to play the violin. She needed to be in contact with those who harbored no evil in their soul; to show them the noble road of the notes, of music: the only companion that would always provide them with happiness and solace, no matter what happened in their lives. Through these children she would always remember her own… the ones she never knew.



How much time had gone by? Countless years, distant, peaceful in appearance, in which she had tried without success to reconstruct her soul's dissonant melodies. No one could suspect her perennial struggle to forget, to forgive, and to not go insane. Tired of wandering on her own nightmarish labyrinths, to wrestle against that relentless loneliness that never dissipated, she was convinced that her wounds would never heal, even if she lived a thousand years. "How curious, Ilse and I have never spoken of what occurred to us. We numbed our memories to ignore them, as if by doing so we could pretend that nothing ever happened, surely so as not to further hurt ourselves," she thought with sadness.

***

When they left Auschwitz and reached the Gare de Paris-Est, they saw how people approached the trains, desperately, with pictures of their relatives, asking if anyone had seen them with hopes of finding them alive. They no longer doubted that their loved ones were dead. Lead shuddered when she recalled what she thought back then: "At least they have pictures; I don't have a single one of mine and with time I will forget their faces." And that is how it was. She hardly remembered her parents' and sister's features. In time, they had become diluted images. She could hardly recall her children. She had only seen them briefly upon their birth and they were also dead. "How would my life be if they had survived? To have someone to love, to live for!" she thought.

For two days they didn't dare leave the train station. They felt lost but pretended to be alive. Neither had they anywhere to go, just like the rest of people that walked like automatons from one end of the station's large hall to the other. From their filthy and emaciated appearance it was plain that many, like themselves, were concentration camp survivors. Some French women walked amongst them, handing out water, hot chocolate, bread, and words of encouragement.



Red Cross officials entered the train station and began identifying the refugees to send them to the Hotel Lutecia, turned into a shelter. Leah and Ilse immediately got in line. The officials took their pictures and information and issued them a sort of passport or identity card, a small white piece of cardboard, with a stamped picture that from then on they'd have to carry as identification.

On their first night at the hotel they hardly could sleep, despite the room's comfort and cleanliness. Both were tormented by the knowledge that, during those years, life had taken its course without them. What was worse, some people had been oblivious to what happened around them, out of ignorance or even worse, indifference. When they finally were able to get some sleep, they were awoken by nightmares —believing still to be in Auschwitz— and insomnia would seize the night. The sensation of once again feeling human was alien to them. A bed, clean clothes, towels, cutlery, food, being tired, a pleasant place to live, the possibility of again harboring hopes… Everything seemed strange to them.

From the hotel's window could be seen several anti-aircraft machine guns pointed to the sky. Paris had been liberated, but the Germans refused to surrender in the Atlantic coast. The Allied airplanes often flew over the city. Occasionally, sirens blasted an aerial alarm and people ran for shelter.

Paris was no longer the City of Light; it didn't look like the one in Leah's memories. It was shrouded in a decadent air, of sadness, gloom, buildings in darkness. Altered by the war, ruin and neglect was evident on the streets. Since gasoline was scarce, cars hardly circulated in the city and bicycles were plentiful. The windows of the few open shops were empty. Movie theaters began to offer limited shows and, in some hotels, the movement of foreigners could be seen.

Allied soldiers moved about in groups and were all over the place: the Canadians with white gaiters and berets tilted to one side; the Scots with checkered kilts and bonnets. Americans seemed to have taken over the city. Wearing helmets, white belts, clubs, guns and handcuffs hanging from their belts, the military police pretended to impose order. The French gendarmes, in blue uniforms, dragged their feet as if they were very tired.

The metro's tunnels were crowded with an anonymous mass of refugees dying of hunger and helplessness. Even though charitable organizations handed out soup and crackers, some lacked the strength to move or eat. Others simply were not interested in going on living.

Anti-Semitism pervaded, and Jews feared for their lives. A lot of European borders were closed for fear of an invasion by refugees coming from concentration camps. The Joint —an organization to help Jewish refugees that had just re-opened its Paris offices— distributed clothes, food, and oversaw travel arrangements for refugees going to other cities to reunite with their relatives. Other charitable organizations joined forces, offering professional training to help people develop skills so they could reincorporate into the workforce as quickly as possible.



Palestine was not the best option, from a risk point of view. The Jews that already lived there, in the settlement of *Yishuv*, organized the *Aliyah Bet*, an illegal mobilization of hundreds of thousands of European refugees that tried to get there by ship. The English government intercepted the boats, preventing their entrance into Palestine, and sent them to detention camps in Cyprus. The survivors' organization, the Sh'erit ha-Pletah, pressured the English, unsuccessfully. The same happened with the United States, which had great restrictions to admit immigrants. It took years for them to progressively augment the quotas of Jews coming from camps.

At first, Ilse and Leah wanted to stay in Paris. The Joint placed them in an attic with a tiny balcony next to the Place Victor Hugo, in a neighborhood teeming with writers, painters, musicians and all kinds of artists… all poor, hungry and disinherited from life themselves.

One afternoon, the bells of Notre Dame —which the French called Marie Thérèse— began pealing incessantly. All remarked surprised that they had not been heard since the beginning of the war. People burst out onto the streets and the Place de la Concord, in an enthusiastic parade where utterances heard everywhere of *Vive la France!* The Town Hall Square was full of Allied flags. De Gaulle came out onto the balcony and said: "Fellow citizens, let's sing the

*Marseillaise*!" The multitudinous chorus, with church bells as accompaniment, lifted everyone's spirits as if by magic. Paris, little by little, awoke from its lethargy.

Germany surrendered on October 7$^{th}$, 1945, but the war raged on in several places on the planet. The great majority didn't seem to care anymore. All they yearned for was to survive, get on with their lives and forget. Leah got a job not far from where they lived in Le chat noir at the rue Leroux, a small club frequented by allied soldiers, but that the French had no access to. For several hours each evening, a young man played the piano and she would join him on the violin. The salary was meager, but it covered the most basic needs. The Joint helped Leah and Ilse with rent. Bread, milk and butter were bought freely, but for the rest they had ration cards. The black market thrived; money was needed to subsist.

Heat was very intense that summer and, little by little, the city began scintillating its legendary lights. The walls —full of graffiti— demanded Pétain's execution, the old traitor, as well as Laval's, the minister who sold out to the Germans. On the 15$^{th}$ of August, several days after the United States' attack on Hiroshima and Nagasaki, the radio broadcasted Emperor Hiroito's message in which he announced Japan's surrender.

The city's sirens blasted insistently at noon. Leah believed that the Germans had returned and ran for shelter. Then she heard the screams on the street: *"La guerre est finie!"* and *"Vive la France!"* Strangers embraced, laughed and cried. Paris' newspapers confirmed on their headlines: "The war is over. Peace has returned." That day, celebrations didn't seem to have an end in all the city's corners. During the night, at Le chat noir, Leah and the pianist played the *Marseillaise* dozens of times. People sang passionately at the top of their voices. Bottles of wine and champagne were uncorked, one after the other. The party lasted till dawn.

In the middle of so much joy, Leah felt disconcerted. More than ever, she needed to be alone. She leaved the club and began to wander aimlessly, crossed the Victor Hugo Square and descended the Poincaré Avenue till the Trocadero. An amazing night, decked up with a full moon that also seemed to be celebrating.



Upon reaching the Palais de Chaillot, Leah sat on a bench, with her back to the pond. Before her, on the Seine, the imposing Pont d'léna, with its famous sculptures of the four warriors: the Gallic, the Roman, the Arab and the Greek. Beyond, the Eiffel Tower, standing majestically before the Champ de Mars and far away, amid the fog, she saw people running and shouting, but could not hear their voices. They seemed to be moving like in a slow-motion film.

Leah remained there for several hours, in silence, submerged in her anguish. She sought peace in the night's solitude, full of conflicting feelings, of sadness and rage for what she had lost, incapable of overcoming the pain of her own life. Knowing that her memories would always be alive within her, that they'd never leave, she would have to learn to forgive and once again believe in others. Like something out of reach, she allowed for the sharp presence of her longing for children to disappear, to infinity.

Humming a *scherzo* on her way home and witnessing upon daybreak glimpses of a world on its road to peace, she finally concluded that without music, her life would be lacking direction and meaning.

Days later, while walking carefree down the street, Leah bumped into a woman she knew: Anika, one of the *boklovas* of Auschwitz, the one who walked like an elephant and who had prevented Rachel and her to be by their mother's side in her last moments. On realizing that she had been recognized, the woman picked up her pace. Leah grabbed her by the arm and vented with fury that she knew who she was. The woman pulled away violently and denied it. Leah began to scream: "Murderer, murderer, stop her! That woman is a Nazi murderer!" People crowded around them. Anika ran and vanished behind the corner.

From that moment on, Leah saw Nazis everywhere. Sometimes she thought she saw Mandel, at other times Grese, Höess… and others whose names she wanted to ignore. What she would never shut out were the faces, those indelible traits which she had seen countless times shoving people towards the gas chambers. Those would remain engraved in her memory for the rest of her life.

A month later, the Joint offered Ilse a job as an assistant nurse in the Amiens hospital, a small village not far from Paris. Leah, although without a job there, decided to accompany her. Paris was still wounded by the war and would not recover in a long time. Besides, it offered the conditions of a big city with lots of people, ideal for the Nazis to hide. They didn't think it over twice; they urgently needed a quiet place where they could start all over again.

The Red Cross paid for the fare to Amiens and put them up in a small hostel. Ilse's salary was not very large, but they had gotten used to living with very little and it would be enough for both, at least at the beginning. Two months later, they moved to a small house in the Saint Maurice neighborhood, close to the hospital where Ilse worked. They had few belongings, but for them it was paradise. Little by little they retook the reins of their lives.



When rumor spread that there was a violin teacher in the village, students flocked in droves. Leah enjoyed the kids' company. She found pleasure in wakening the curiosity of music in them and basked in their amazement at their capacity to produce sounds on a violin. She soon had to cut back on the number of students because the hours in the day didn't suffice.

Three years later, Ilse married Philippe Sprinz, a Jewish engineer and an Amiens resident. Philippe had been a prisoner in the Theresienstadt Concentration Camp, where he also lost his parents and brothers. A very simple wedding was celebrated by a rabbi friend of theirs in the presence of Leah and a few intimate acquaintances. They had two sons: Cyprien and Vincent, who addressed Leah as "aunt" and whom she considered her nephews.

Accompanied by two black cats she picked off the street, Leah moved to a smaller house in the Saint Leu neighborhood, where she opened her studio. She adored teaching her pupils. Wholeheartedly and bursting with flowers, she took care of a little garden in front of her house. Just like in her Bremen home, Leah loved to practice her violin underneath a gigantic tree.

She often wondered what could have happened to her Guarneri. How much she missed its sound! The last time she held it in her hands was also the last time she saw her sister. Leah was sure that Mengele had destroyed it, like he had done with everything she loved.

At six in the morning and at six in the afternoon she would listen to the bells of the gothic cathedral. Since the house was centric, she could walk through the city, stroll around the area of the Somme River and move about everywhere without difficulty. She was happy in Amiens, as long as she could keep her ghosts at bay. Various suitors approached her, as she had become a very pretty woman. About to marry the village's veterinarian, Leah broke it off at the last minute and decided to stay single. She felt incapable of loving, as if happiness were forbidden to her. The omnipresent guilt of having survived haunted her.

They were banging at the door with the impatience. Ilse had arrived.

***

"I came to talk to you," Ilse said nervously.

"What's the matter? You're pale."

Ilse, anxious, could not find the adequate words or how to begin, knowing perfectly well that what she was about to disclose would unleash a terrible storm upon her dear friend. She sat down beside her on the sofa and spoke to her, in a paused tone of voice, trying in vain to look as serene as possible:

"A while ago I received the visit of a man who is presently looking for you. He asked me if you had delivered twins during your stay in Auschwitz and if I knew your address. He claims to be your son."

"No, Ilse, it can't be. My son died!" Leah reacted, incredulous, wringing her hands.

"Leah, listen to me."

"No, Ilse, no, it's a mistake!"

"Please, Leah, think it over. That man could very well be your son."

"Why do you think that? My son is dead!"

Ilse then gave account about Alex and Mariana's visit, how they found out about his adoption, and the intense search that had driven them to her.

"When the director of the hospital called me, I was very surprised; especially since it was you they were looking for. I authorized him to give them my number and address. I thought it worthwhile to know what it was all about and decided to meet him. When we spoke, he asked a lot of questions about you. He's sure you're his mother."

"Could it be possible?" Leah asked herself, surprised. She had never permitted herself to think her son would be alive. When that faint possibility surfaced before, she discarded it immediately, as she imagined her son to be a sinister monster like his father. Leah was confused; her melodious world had disrupted in a senseless counterpoint.

"What else did he tell you?"

"He urgently needs to see you."

"Didn't he mention who raised him?"

"Only that he was adopted by an American soldier and his wife."

"Wasn't it Mengele by any chance? Perhaps it was he who took him away from the camp, pretending to be someone else. He must be alive."

"Leah, Mengele died years ago in Brazil."

"That's what they say, but I don't know if it's true. His whereabouts were always a mystery. For years, I was scared to bump into him on the street or that he'd search for me. Sometimes I thought I saw him on street corners. It is said that he moved from one place to another in South America. I don't even have the certainty he's dead."

"I know you always thought about the possibility of him having taken your son. Even I believed it at some point. Now it seems that child didn't die after all, and that Mengele fled alone. Maybe he transferred the child to some other place or ordered the nurse that took care of him to drop him off at some hospital, and this is how he was given up for adoption. Of course, all this is mere speculation."

"I'm scared, Ilse, very scared. What if he rejects me? What if he reproaches me for not having looked for him?" Leah's hands trembled.

"Remember I was with you when we returned to Auschwitz to look for him and when they informed you that he had died. Even if you had believed that he was alive, you would've not been able to locate him. You were also a victim; you must face up to this reality and to your own fears. Please, don't punish yourself anymore."

Leah was devastated. She couldn't believe what was taking place. The fear, which she thought was under control, once again took hold of her. For years she had been trying to live in peace with her loneliness and her memories. She thought she had achieved it and now the past returned to torment her.

"I'm scared, I'm scared…" Leah repeated crying, while Ilse hugged her.

"Your son looks like a good person. You must meet him; you both need to talk. It's a chapter of this story that must come to a close. Don't you agree?"

"He's going to ask who his father was," Leah said in anguish.

"Then, you must tell him."

"I don't know if I must; I don't think I'm capable. It's going to be awful for him to discover whose son he is…"

"Leah, he has a right to know."

"What's his name?"

"Alex York."

"Like the pianist?" Leah asked surprised.

"He's *the* pianist."

"Are you sure? He's one of the best in the world! I went to Paris a year ago to a concert of his. Remember that your son Vincent accompanied me?"

"It's him. When he revealed his name, I asked him to prove it. Look, here's his card. He wants to see you this very day. He's desperate…"

"Is he coming today? I'm not sure."

"I agreed to call him as soon as I spoke to you. I will coordinate the meeting for this afternoon at four o'clock here, in your house. He's coming with his girlfriend, Mariana."

"Ilse, Ilse, I'm so scared…"

"Dear Leah, all will go well. You'll see."

"You will be present, right?"

"Of course, I'll be here with you. I always have, haven't I?"

The two women hugged one another in silence.

***



"Mariana, I can hardly believe that all this is true. Just recently my life ran smoothly, but now it turns out that I was adopted, have no idea who my father was and don't know my real mother. It's like madness."

"You will soon clear everything up, Alex. We are going to meet her shortly. Your mother has a pretty name: Leah Felton. I can assure you she too is surprised. Perhaps she thought you were dead."

"She could have looked for me, don't you think?"

"Alex, you have to listen to her story first, which must be horrible, as having been in Auschwitz in itself. You were in that place and you know you cannot judge her. What happened to her is beyond our comprehension and it must've been very traumatic for her. She was very young, almost a girl. You must be patient and compassionate with her. Listen and accept what she must tell you, no matter how terrible it may be. Remember it's your mother and has suffered a lot. You, in spite of it all, had parents that loved you and gave you all the opportunities."

"You're right, I'm sorry. It's just that I am in a daze. I feel very sad, everything feels so alien, as if weren't happening to me. And, nevertheless, it's true; I am very scared of meeting her. Don't know why..."

"It's understandable. All this is very strange. You always wondered where your love for music came from. Well, you see, your mother is a violinist..."

"Well, if that's something you inherit…"

"Do you fancy your father was a musician as well?"

"That's one of the questions I am going to ask her. I want to know everything. Are you sure you've got the correct address? We don't know the village well, and it's almost time to be there."

"Yes, I have the directions Ilse gave me here. Calm down, please. We are close."

"Please let's not drag this out any further. I am desperate to get there," Alex said nervously.

***

Leah walked around from one end of the room to the other. Ilse looked at her with a smile.

"Come on, Leah, relax. He'll soon be here. You're very anxious."

"I can't avoid it. Never in a million years, I thought this would ever happen to me. What do you think he will think of me? Do I look okay?"

"For God's sake, woman, don't torture you like that! I'm sure he's a good man and will immediately realize that you are a marvelous lady. Besides, you look lovely."

"Did you explain to him how to get here?"

"Yes. He was very nervous and asked that I give the address to his girlfriend who, by the way, is very kind. They must be about to arrive, it's almost four."

Knocking at the door, Ilse rushed to answer.

"Good afternoon, Ilse," said Alex, entering with Mariana.

With a faltering step —his hands shaking— he came up to Leah.



"I'm Alex, your son," he said softly.

"My son..." Leah repeated in a low voice, as in a whisper.

Leah looked at him incredulously. The man now standing before her says he's the son she thought had lost. Suddenly, she heard the forgotten melodies. The music invaded her head once again, reminiscing the days when she was innocent and happy. The *agitato impetuoso* of a *concerto grosso*, untranslatable in words, broke forth in all her senses. Her heartbeat joined in with the music's rhythm. She had never dared to dream of her son being alive and now she was staring at him, face-to-face.

And without being able to utter any more words, both held each other in a long, long embrace. Ilse and Mariana were deeply moved, watching the scene.

Alex and Leah contemplated each other with curiosity. She was shaken and perplexed, looking at his face and to his pianist's hands. "He has the profile of my sister, mother's eyes, and father's bearing," she said to herself. Through him, she had recovered the memory of her loved ones.

Looking carefully at the woman he had just met, Alex was struck by the kindness she emanated. He saw himself reflected in her. "The brand of the virtuoso," he thought, after noticing the shadow of the violin's grazing on his mother's neck. Intangible, endless currents flowed between them which turned into an indestructible bond of blood and melodies. They connected in a perfect tessitura, like in an antiphonal canto in which each one tries to identify in the other a trait of one's self.

"You must be Mariana, Alex's girlfriend," Leah said coming up to her, as they embraced.

With delicacy, trying to conceal her emotions, Ilse interrupted: "You two must have a lot to talk about."

Mariana and Ilse, in a tacit agreement and without exchanging any words, left the room. Mother and son needed to be alone.

"There is a lot I need to know, mother. I don't know what to ask you and where to begin," he confessed, very nervous.

Drying her tears, Leah consented and said to Alex: "Please, tell me everything about your childhood, who were your adoptive parents, if you loved them a lot, where did you live..."

Alex sat by her side, held her hands and confided:

"I will do so and will tell you my life in detail. For now, please just let me assure you that I had wonderful parents who loved me very much. We have an entire lifetime to talk, but first you must tell me the truth. You have my word I'll make no reproaches nor judge you. I was in Auschwitz looking for you and can imagine what you must have suffered, even though it will be difficult to understand for those of us who didn't live through it. Please, don't hide anything from me, no matter how horrific it may be. Especially, I need you to reveal who my father was," Alex said to her, moved with bloodshot eyes and in a controlled voice.

Caressing the pianist's hands, Leah looked at Alex lovingly. Getting closer to him, with a slight quiver in her voice and in syncopated rhythm, she whispered into his ear in a tone of confession:

"That afternoon father arrived with the news..."

# CODA – Buenos Aires, 2003

"How pleasant it is to walk around the San Telmo Fair! Let's go to Claudio's kiosk, to see what new things he's got," Alex said with enthusiasm.

They walked in-between other kiosks decorated with a multitude of objects, surrounded by a mass of curious and buyers. A rhythmic tango could be heard in the back and in a corner a couple gave a demonstration of the dance. The screams from the salesmen with their assorted merchandise seasoned the afternoon.

"Ah, Alex, I forgot to tell you that Armand called last night after the concert, while you were busy with your admirers signing autographs," Mariana said.

"No doubt to ask me how it went, as he always does. He must miss those years in which he accompanied me. I, too, miss his presence."

"He also called to give us a piece of good news: America is pregnant again."

"They're on their fourth," Alex remarked.

***

Alex was devastated when he confirmed the truth about his origin and the identity of his father. Mariana was the greatest support in helping him to overcome the impact. Besides, his musical sensibility enabled him to understand that the only thing that mattered —to compensate for so much suffering— was the love his mother deserved. Before the marvelous connection between mother and son in knowing each other was established, and after all the confessions, they agreed ever again to speak of the past. All that mattered was the future, to make up for the lost time.

A little after that first meeting with his mother, Alex and Mariana remarried in Puerto Rico in a very intimate ceremony. Leah was fascinated with the beauty of the island and the hospitality of its people. She afterwards returned several times with them so that his son could show him the places where he'd grown up.

They convinced Leah to retire and move to Paris in an apartment next to theirs. Mariana became a daughter for her. After so many years of loneliness, Leah could not believe she had a family. She would often visit Ilse in Amiens, where she had also left behind lots of affection.

Alex would often organize musical soirées and would ask his mother to perform with him on the violin. Leah ended up playing before world-renowned musicians, friends of her son, who praised her virtuosity. She felt radiant, happy. She only missed her Guarnerius, but never uttered a word about it.

As he had promised Mariana, Alex cut back on the number of concerts and quit undertaking the marathon tours of the past. He accepted the Music Director position of the Paris Symphony Orchestra. Leah would accompany them when he performed sporadic concerts in different countries. When he finished playing and stood up from the stool to greet the audience, his first eye contact —a wink, a smile— was directed to his mother, his most faithful admirer. Alex knew where to find her: in the first row, euphoric, applauding with enthusiasm.



On the birth of her granddaughter, Leah said it was the best present she had ever received in her entire life. No sooner was the girl able to walk, she put a small toy violin in her hands and a few years later she took formal charge of her music classes. Leah would say with pride: "This girl has talent and will be a violinist." Grandmother and granddaughter adored each other and would spend many hours sharing their passion for music. Throughout the years, Leah would remark that her granddaughter, of reddish hair, blue eyes and turned up nose, had transfigured into the vivid image of Vera, her mother.

***

"Do you remember that today marks three years since Leah died?" Yesterday, when you performed the piano concerto she loved the most, I couldn't stop thinking about her," Mariana said.

"Of course I remember, that's why I chose to perform that work. As a matter-of-fact, mother is in my mind every day. If life had not betrayed her, she could have been a great soloist. She was cut out to be a female virtuoso."

"Leah was so proud of you! She would often tell me that you had inherited her talent."

"I admired mother immensely. She was a great woman. I am happy to have brought and shared with her a little bit of joy during her last years."

***



Leah had sworn she would never return to Germany but, in 1999, Alex persuaded her to accompany them to Berlin for a concert he would offer on occasion of the commemoration of the sixtieth anniversary of the crossing of the *St. Louis*, sixty-one years of the Kristallnacht, and the tenth anniversary of the fall of the Berlin Wall.

The Konzerthaus turned out in its finest. Alex played Chopin's "*Heroic Polonaise*" and Prokofiev's Sonata No. 1 in F Minor, op. 1 and, as an *encore*, Scriabin's "*Pathétique*" Étude in D-sharp Minor. Prior to beginning the concert and before the Prime Minister and dignitaries from all around the world, Alex addressed the hall to honor the presence of his mother as a German survivor of the Holocaust. Leah cried during the entire concert, but she afterwards admitted that having returned to her country had been a catharsis which had helped her heal her wounds.

They also visited Bremen. Leah showed them where her father's practice stood, as well as her old house, now turned into an art school. Her granddaughter asked her many questions and Leah was happy to be able to take them to places where she'd spent her childhood. At first she was uncertain, but afterwards gained confidence and was finally able to laugh.

Leah was very happy during her last years. When she passed away, at 78, she left a huge void in the lives of those who got to know her. In fact, Leah's prediction came to fruition: her granddaughter had inherited her talent. A beautiful young lady now, she was determined to become a soloist, as she had promised her grandmother.

***



"Come, my love, we're almost there," Mariana called her young daughter, who got distracted a bit further up looking at antiquities, so she'd come into the old musical instruments section at the kiosk they habitually frequented when visiting Buenos Aires.

"Is Claudio in?" Alex asked the man in charge.

"No, I am Enrique, his nephew. My uncle is not feeling well, he's at home."

"I am sorry to hear that. I came to say hello to him and see if he had anything new. Claudio is very knowledgeable about music and always has interesting things."

"Are you Maestro York?"

"Yes, how do you know?"

"Because my uncle read in the newspaper that last night you were playing at the Colón Theater. He was sure that today you would come by the kiosk and told me to call him when you asked for him."

The young man proceeded to dial a number and then handed the cell phone over to Alex. Both held a short conversation.

"Let's go to Claudio's house. He told me that he's retiring from the business and wants to say goodbye to us," Alex told his wife and daughter.

"My uncle is very old and so is his wife. Since they didn't have children, I convinced them to retire and come with me to Córdoba —where I live with my family— to look after them. There they have a small house next to ours. Today is the last operational day of the shop and I'm selling off all the merchandise," the man remarked.



"Allow me to see those scores," Alex said, referring to a bunch lying in a corner. He glanced at them, and then bought some old ones that seemed interesting.

"Do you know where my uncle lives?"

"Yes, of course, close by. We have visited him a few times in the past."

They headed to the old man's house, who received them with great joy. His wife was out. As they were preparing to move, there were boxes everywhere.

"Hello, Claudio, what's that about you retiring and going to Cordoba…?"

"It´s nature's law, Maestro, I am an old man, and it's time to retire. Hello, Mariana, so nice to see you again. But, is this your daughter? How tall she's grown in these two last years, since we last saw each other. You're a young grown-up lady! How old are you now?"

"I am about to turn sixteen, Don Claudio."

"Do you still play the violin?"

"Yes, my first recital is in three months' time. I'm very excited."

"Surely you practice a lot."

"You can't imagine, Claudio. She doesn't let go of the violin. We have to tell her to rest," Mariana remarked.

"Do you know what? In my youth I also played the violin, but I no longer can because of the arthritis in my fingers..." the old man told the youngster, with a note of nostalgia.

Claudio got up from his stool and, with a faltering step, headed to a contiguous room. He came back with a violin under his arm.



"Let's see," he said to the young girl, "play something for this old man."

The girl took the instrument in her hands. She examined it carefully. It looked old and the wood had several scratches, but it was lovely. She adjusted the pegs to check the tuning, placed it in position and brandished the bow with skill and determination. She played Massenet's *Meditation from Thaïs*, with which she planned to conclude her concert.

That instrument of clear timbre awoke in her an unexplainable enthusiasm. She was enraptured with the delightful diaphaneity of its sound that didn't resemble any of the ones she'd ever held in her hands.

Don Claudio listened to her carefully, thoughtfully, with a serious expression. The young girl's skill was evident. Her face had transformed, her fibers vibrated at the music's beat. Like a good connoisseur, Don Claudio was immediately convinced he was witnessing a profusion of virtuosity, and a great promise. The young girl brought out the best in the instrument. When she was done with the interpretation, he applauded and enthusiastically told her:

"Brava! You're going to go far. You must've noticed that violin is special, right? As you can imagine, I know a little about music and an instrument like that needs a performer like you. I give it to you. Use it in your first concert and remember me that day."

The young girl, surprised, looked at her parents. She didn't know whether to jump in the air out of sheer joy, hug the man, or remain quiet. Sure enough, her affinity with that violin had been immediate: on playing it, she felt deeply moved. It was the most incredible sound she had ever produced while playing on any violin.



Alex and Mariana looked perplexed at the old man's action. They knew what that present meant to their daughter

"But Claudio, that violin must be priceless. Its sonority is extraordinary!" Alex said.

"The material side matters little to me, Maestro. I have never placed too much interest in money, and now, at my age, even less. In due time, your daughter will give it its real value, as she produces melodies with it and offers them to her public."

"Why would you get rid of your violin?" Alex replied.

"I am going to tell you this story... Some thirty years ago, a man came to see me and pawned this violin. He begged me not to sell it because he would return forthwith to pick it up, but did not do so. I never wanted to part with it because I immediately realized it was a great instrument. When I die, no one is going to appreciate it the way I do, it is my pleasure to give it to your daughter, Maestro. I have just confirmed that she's very talented and studies with devotion, so it couldn't be in better hands. She has the perfect formula for a great musician: virtuosity and discipline. I am sure this violin is going to tour the world's most important concert halls. She will know how to appreciate and treasure it."

"What a great honor, Claudio! But, please, let me pay you for it. I am sure it's very good."

"Out of the question, I already told you it was a present won't accept anything else. You know what a stubborn old man I am. All I ask is that she plays it in her first concert, and that she sends me a picture," he said firmly and with a smile.



"Of course, Don Claudio, I shall do so. I am very grateful! You can't imagine how happy you've made me," the young girl answered with a broad smile, while she hugged the old man with affection, who was also moved and on the brink of tears.

"Maestro, I recommend you take the violin to a good luthier to have him look it over and make the proper adjustments."

"As soon as we return to Paris, I'll take it to Pavonni. He is my friend."

"The old Pavonni... I know who he is – one of the best. He will certify its quality. Please convey my regards and do tell him to call me."

"A million thanks, Claudio. You're very generous."

"Here, this will be my address and telephone in Cordoba. If you ever go that way, to play or for pleasure, make sure you call on me."

When they were about to leave, Don Claudio told them:

"Wait! I was forgetting something!"

With an unsteady step, he headed back towards the room. Bringing with him a threadbare case, of an undefined color, he placed the instrument inside it and handed it to the young girl while telling her:

"The case is in deplorable condition, and you will need to replace it. I suppose you will buy a new one, but at least for now it will serve you to carry it."

They bid the old man farewell, reiterating their gratefulness and returned to the hotel. On their way back and with an iridescent grin on her face, the girl held tightly to her instrument. She was ecstatic; couldn't believe the violin was hers. All three commented on the old man's kind action. The plane would leave in a few hours on their return trip to their Paris' home.

No sooner had they stepped into the hotel room, the girl, very enthusiastic, sat down on the sofa and opened the case to examine the violin.

"Mother, father... Come quick!"

"What's the matter, love?"

The case has my name…"

# Music glossary of *Concert for Leah**

16 - *Liebesträume*, by Liszt, S. 541/3; R. 211/3. Piano work popularly, known as *Dream of Love*. It is the last of a set of three nocturnes, in A-flat major, based on a transcription of the song *O lieb, so lang du lieben kannst*.

25 - *Horst-Wessel-Lied* by Horst Ludwig Wessel, a Nazi activist. It became the Nazi Party anthem from 1930 to 1945. It is also known as *Die Fahne hoch* ("The Flag On High"), which comprise the opening words of the anthem.

34 - *Freut euch des Lebens,* a festive German waltz composed by Johan Strauss II.

60 - *Totentanz,* or Dance of the Dead, based on the Gregorian plainchant melody of the *Dies iræ*, the liturgy of the mass for the deceased.

68 - *Petrushka*, by Stravinsky. Three movements from the ballet transcribed into a suite for piano solo. It is one of the most difficult and technically demanding works of the twentieth-century piano literature.

---

* Music consultant: José Cáceres Danielsen, pianist.

80 - Piano Concerto No. 3 in D Minor, op. 30, by Rachmaninoff, a titanic, fiendishly difficult staple of the twentieth-century piano concerti repertoire.

80 - Waltz in D-flat Major, op. 64, no. 1, by Chopin, also known as the "Minute Waltz."

91 - *Novosvětská* or Symphony No. 9 in E Minor, op. 95, by Dvořák, composed in 1893 during his visit to the United States. This work is best known as the "New World" Symphony or "From the New World."



129 - Chaconne from the Partita No. 2 in D Minor for Solo Violin, BWV 1004, by J. S. Bach.

131 - *The Merry Widow*, operetta by the Austro-Hungarian composer Franz Lehár.

131 - "Barcarolle" based on tunes by the Venetian gondoliers. The most well-known is the one by Offenbach from his opera *The Tales of Hoffmann.*

131 - Waltzes by Johann Strauss II.

131 - *Czárdás*, by Vittorio Monti, based on the dance forms from the Hungarian folklore.

132 - Caprice No. 16 from the Twenty-Four Caprices for Solo Violin, by Paganini.

132 - "Un bel di vedremo." Aria from the opera *Madama Butterfly*, by Puccini.

132 - Suite No. 1 for Unaccompanied Violoncello, BWV 1007, by J. S. Bach.

132 - Third Movement from Dvořák´s Concerto for Cello and Orchestra in B Minor, op. 104.

132 - Overture from *Mastersingers of Nuremberg*, by Wagner.

136 - *Deutsche Eichen* or the German Oaks, a German song.

137 - *Kol Nidre, a* Jewish prayer recited prior to the beginning of the evening service of Yom Kippur. It takes its name from the initial words of the prayer. Its melody has been the basis and inspiration for composers like Arnold Schoenberg, Max Bruch and John Zorn.



149 - *Fantasiestücke, op. 73,* set of eight pieces for piano solo by Robert Schumann.

150 - *Andante* from the Sonata for Violin No. 2 in A Minor, BWV 1003, by J. S. Bach.

152 - *The Ring of the Nibelung*, by Wagner, a part of the cycle of four epic operas based on elements and characters of the Germanic mythology.

153 - *Après une Lecture de Dante: Fantasia quasi Sonata* by Liszt, S.161/7; R.10/7. One-movement piano sonata inspired by the *Divine Comedy*, by Dante Alighieri, a technically and interpretatively demanding nineteenth-century piano work.

153 - Madrigal, secular music to complement brief and delicate lyrical texts. The most well-known madrigal composers are Claudius Monteverdi, Carlo Gesualdo and Luca Marenzio.

154 - *Rondo* from the Sonata in D Major for Violin and Piano, op. 12, no. 1, by Beethoven, a work of noticeable nuances and contrasts.

157 - *Twilight of the Gods*, by Wagner, the last work from the cycle of four operas that forms part of *The Ring of the Nibelung.*

167 - *Ein deutsches Requiem, op. 45,* by Brahms, a funeral cantata comprised of seven parts, composed for soprano, baritone, mixed choir and orchestra.

177 - *Meditation from Thaïs,* by Massenet. This fragment, for violin solo with orchestral accompaniment, is part of the opera *Thaïs.*

196 - *La Marseillaise,* National anthem of France.

212 - "Heroic Polonaise" or Polonaise in A-flat major, op. 53, by Chopin, one of the most recognizable polonaises from this composer.

212 - Piano Sonata No.1 in F Minor, op. 1, by Prokofiev, it is a single-movement piano sonata.

212 - Étude in D-sharp Minor, op. 8, no. 12, ("Pathétique"), by Scriabin, a Russian composer.

Saint Louis ship at Havana bay,
surrounded by several small boats.

The event of the *Saint Louis*, in 1939, marked a dark page in Cuba's history. It has never been determined with certainty why the Cuban government decided to return it to Europe with its cargo of almost a thousand Jews, among them 158 children, who were fleeing from the Nazis and who had their documents in order. At least 254 adults and 33 children died in the extermination camps.

Many theories have been elaborated, from the idea that they were victims of political rivalries and the corruption that existed in Cuba, to the possibility that it was caused by an anti-Semitic campaign orchestrated by the Nazis to demonstrate that, although they allowed the Jews to leave Germany, the democratic countries in America had no disposition to receive them.

Although the *Saint Louis* received great world-wide media coverage at that moment, to my surprise, many readers have commented that they did not know about it. Perhaps the later events that ended in World War II cast a shadow over this tragic event. Today, at almost 80 years of that fateful journey, the few survivors left are some of the children who went on board.

The history of the *Saint Louis* has always produced disbelief and sadness in me. To incorporate it to this novel is my tribute to each one of those innocent people who fled from the oppressive regime that threatened their freedom and their lives.

The author

## Comments by some readers

"As soon as I began reading it caught my attention immediately. I could not drop it. This happens to me with few books. The author treats the subject in an ingenious form, with a great amount of data faithful to history."

"With direct and simple language, this novel shakes the reader and leaves him/her thinking. The symbiosis between music and emotions gives a poetic touch to it. It is evident the deep work of investigation carried out by the author."

"It has cadence, strength, love, hate. The notes are crowded in the reader's throat and devastate everything. The reader feels as if he were in the middle of the action. It let me with the desire of reading more. The finale is impeccable."

"Tremendous narrative force, the images are described as in a movie. It is electrifying. The musical touch makes the plot less terrible."

"This novel is an impressive combination of melodies and words. With a simple and precise vocabulary, this terrible history does not lack Leah's tender and honest touch. When cruelty becomes a protagonist, the narration and the description are heartrending."

"The music in this novel is a great success; a very difficult task to achieve. While I read it, I listened to several of the pieces that are mentioned here and it was an indescribable experience. This is one of those works that one will always remember."

## Opinion by some writers

"The writer imparts to her book the force that only true literature can obtain: the credibility of the narrated issue. From sensitivity and a deep humanism, *Concert for Leah* makes a notch in literary history on the subject of the Nazi Holocaust."

AMIR VALLE

Cuban writer living in Berlin.

"Nobody comes out unharmed after facing a world war and human extermination seen from the eyes of a girl. The notes on the staff gather to form sounds, and they become the audible representation of Leah's soul. We can 'read' and 'listen to' her feelings."

JOSE IGNACIO VALENZUELA

Chilean writer and scriptwriter.

"It is an architectonic novel like few, with a shining musical substrate. It is, without any doubt, "a must," one of those books that cannot be left aside once you start reading."

DANIEL TORRES

Puerto Rican writer and university professor
in the United States.

"The chapters follow one after the other as if they were episodes, with endings that take us to wonder: what will happen next? When moving to a next chapter the time jumps continue, in which scenes and characters alternate."

MARGARITA BRAVO IGUINA
Puerto Rican writer.

"The story, increasingly suffocating and terrible, makes this novel a highly recommended one. It is very agile, straight to the point, with temporary location jumps and changes in the narrative voice. There is no doubt that many more editions of the book will be printed."

MARTA FARRERAS
Chemistry of profession and Spanish reviewer.

"The presence of the Caribbean in the Holocaust would have been unthinkable for some writers. *Concert for Leah* is a lesson for the reader, an excellent novel."

JESSIKA REYES SERRANO
Puerto Rican writer.

"A quality writing that, with elegance and precision at times hallucinating, gives us detailed psychological pictures. The case that locks up this story could have had the name of anyone of us."

Gustavo Sánchez Perdomo
Cuban writer and reviewer living in Paris.

# Biography of Maira Landa

Master's degree in Creative Writing – Sacred Heart University in Puerto Rico. Awarded the "Medalla Pórtico" for academic excellence. Bachelor's degree in Business Administration – University of Puerto Rico.

Her novel, *Concierto para Leah*, was chosen among the ten finalists in 2009 at the prestigious "Premio Planeta" in Barcelona, Spain. The novel placed fifth out of 492 novels submitted worldwide. It also won the PEN Club International Award to the Best Novel published in Puerto Rico in 2010.

Winner of the 2006 literary contest "Manuel Joglar Cacho" sponsored by the Institute of Puerto Rican Culture, earning First Prize in the Short Story Division and Third Prize in the Poetry Division.

President of the Board of Directors of "Salón Literario Libroamérica," which in 2010 celebrated the first Festival de la Palabra in Puerto Rico. This inaugural event rounded up 65 internationally writers and since then is held annually in the island.

In 2012 UNESCO granted her a Diploma for her contribution to the literature in Puerto Rico.

Coordinator and participant in roundtables with several authors at events such as the Puerto Rican International Book Fair, Puerto

Rican National Archives, Puerto Rican Center for Advanced Studies, Sacred Heart University, and Festival de la Palabra, among others. Has chaired presentations of numerous novels as well as literary investigative texts by distinguished authors.

Four-year panelist at the literary radio program "Tardes de Tertulia," where she interviewed numerous distinguished writers.



Born in Havana, Cuba. Writer, businesswoman, and civic leader. After her exile from Cuba, she lived in Caracas, Venezuela. She subsequently moved to San Juan, Puerto Rico, where she currently resides and has been a dynamic contributor in the island's literary scene.

Literary Agent: Antonia Kerrigan, Barcelona, Spain